A2-Level Physics

The Revision Guide

Exam Board: Edexcel

Editors:
Amy Boutal, Sarah Hilton, Alan Rix, Julie Wakeling, Sarah Williams

Contributors
Jane Cartwright, Peter Cecil, Mark A. Edwards, Barbara Mascetti, John Myers, Zoe Nye, Moira Steven, Andy Williams

Proofreaders:
Ian Francis, Glenn Rogers

Published by Coordination Group Publications Ltd.

Many thanks to Professor Peter Watkins at the University of Birmingham for his kind permission to reproduce the photographs used on page 34.

ISBN: 978 1 84762 270 9

Groovy website: www.cgpbooks.co.uk
Jolly bits of clipart from CorelDRAW®
Printed by Elanders Hindson Ltd, Newcastle upon Tyne.

Contents

The Scientific Process

'How Science Works' is all about the scientific process — how we develop and test scientific ideas. It's what scientists do all day, every day (well, except at coffee time — never come between a scientist and their coffee).

Scientists Come Up with **Theories** — Then **Test Them...**

Science tries to explain **how** and **why** things happen — it **answers questions**. It's all about seeking and gaining **knowledge** about the world around us. Scientists do this by **asking** questions and **suggesting** answers and then **testing** them, to see if they're correct — this is the **scientific process**.

1) **Ask** a question — make an **observation** and ask **why or how** it happens. E.g. what is the nature of light?
2) **Suggest** an answer, or part of an answer, by forming:
   - a **theory** (a possible **explanation** of the observations) e.g. light is a wave.
   - a **model** (a **simplified picture** of what's physically going on)
3) Make a **prediction** or **hypothesis** — a **specific testable statement**, based on the theory, about what will happen in a test situation. E.g. light should interfere and diffract.
4) Carry out a **test** — to provide **evidence** that will support the prediction, or help disprove it. E.g. Young's double-slit experiment.

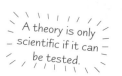

The evidence supported Quentin's Theory of Flammable Burps.

A theory is only scientific if it can be tested.

...Then They **Tell** Everyone About Their **Results...**

The results are **published** — scientists need to let others know about their work. Scientists publish their results in **scientific journals**. These are just like normal magazines, only they contain **scientific reports** (called papers) instead of the latest celebrity gossip.

1) Scientific reports are similar to the **lab write-ups** you do in school. And just as a lab write-up is **reviewed** (marked) by your teacher, reports in scientific journals undergo **peer review** before they're published.
2) The report is sent out to **peers** — other scientists that are experts in the **same area**. They examine the data and results, and if they think that the conclusion is reasonable it's **published**. This makes sure that work published in scientific journals is of a **good standard**.
3) But peer review **can't guarantee** the science is **correct** — other scientists still need to **reproduce** it.
4) Sometimes **mistakes** are made and bad work is published. Peer review **isn't perfect** but it's probably the best way for scientists to self-regulate their work and to publish **quality reports**.

...Then **Other Scientists** Will **Test** the Theory Too

Other scientists read the published theories and results, and try to **test the theory** themselves. This involves:

- Repeating the **exact same experiments**.
- Using the theory to make **new predictions** and then testing them with **new experiments**.

If the **Evidence** Supports a Theory, It's **Accepted — for Now**

1) If all the experiments in all the world provide evidence to back it up, the theory is thought of as **scientific 'fact'** (for now).
2) But they never become **totally undisputable** fact. Scientific **breakthroughs or advances** could provide new ways to question and test the theory, which could lead to **new evidence** that **conflicts** with the current evidence. Then the testing starts all over again...

And this, my friend, is the **tentative nature of scientific knowledge** — it's always **changing** and **evolving**.

The Scientific Process

So scientists need evidence to back up their theories. They get it by carrying out experiments, and when that's not possible they carry out studies. But why bother with science at all? We want to know as much as possible so we can use it to try and improve our lives (and because we're nosey).

Evidence Comes From Controlled Lab Experiments...

1) Results from **controlled experiments** in **laboratories** are **great**.
2) A lab is the easiest place to **control variables** so that they're all **kept constant** (except for the one you're investigating).

For example, finding the charge stored on a capacitor by charging at a constant current and measuring the voltage across it (see p. 12). All other variables need to be kept the same, e.g. the current you use and the temperature, as they may also affect its capacitance.

... That You can Draw Meaningful Conclusions From

"Right Geoff, you can start the experiment now... I've stopped time..."

1) You always need to make your experiments as **controlled** as possible so you can be confident that any effects you see are linked to the variable you're changing.
2) If you do find a relationship, you need to be careful what you conclude. You need to decide whether the effect you're seeing is **caused** by changing a variable, or whether the two are just **correlated**.

Society Makes Decisions Based on Scientific Evidence

1) Lots of scientific work eventually leads to **important discoveries** or breakthroughs that could **benefit humankind**.
2) These results are **used by society** (that's you, me and everyone else) to **make decisions** — about the way we live, what we eat, what we drive, etc.
3) All sections of society use scientific evidence to make decisions, e.g. politicians use it to devise policies and individuals use science to make decisions about their own lives.

Other factors can **influence** decisions about science or the way science is used:

Economic factors

- Society has to consider the **cost** of implementing changes based on scientific conclusions — e.g. the cost of reducing the UK's carbon emissions to limit the human contribution to **global warming**.
- Scientific research is often **expensive**. E.g. in areas such as astronomy, the Government has to **justify** spending money on a new telescope rather than pumping money into, say, the **NHS** or **schools**.

Social factors

- **Decisions** affect **people's lives** — e.g. when looking for a site to build a **nuclear power station**, you need to consider how it would affect the lives of the people in the **surrounding area**.

Environmental factors

- Many scientists suggest that building **wind farms** would be a **cheap** and **environmentally friendly** way to generate electricity in the future. But some people think that because **wind turbines** can **harm wildlife** such as birds and bats, other methods of generating electricity should be used.

So there you have it — how science works...

Hopefully these pages have given you a nice intro to how science works, e.g. what scientists do to provide you with 'facts'. You need to understand this, as you're expected to know how science works yourself — for the exam and for life.

Momentum

These pages are about linear momentum — that's momentum in a straight line (not a circle).

Understanding **Momentum** helps you do **Calculations** on **Collisions**

The **momentum** of an object depends on two things — its **mass** and **velocity**.
The **product** of these two values is the momentum of the object.

Remember, velocity is a vector quantity, so it has size and direction.

momentum = mass × velocity or in symbols: p (in $kg\,ms^{-1}$) = m (in kg) × v (in ms^{-1})

Momentum is always **Conserved**

1) Assuming **no external forces** act, momentum is always **conserved**.
2) This means the **total momentum** of two objects **before** they collide **equals** the total momentum **after** the collision.
3) This is really handy for working out the **velocity** of objects after a collision (as you do...):

Example A skater of mass 75 kg and velocity 4 ms^{-1} collides with a stationary skater of mass 50 kg. The two skaters join together and move off in the same direction. Calculate their velocity after impact.

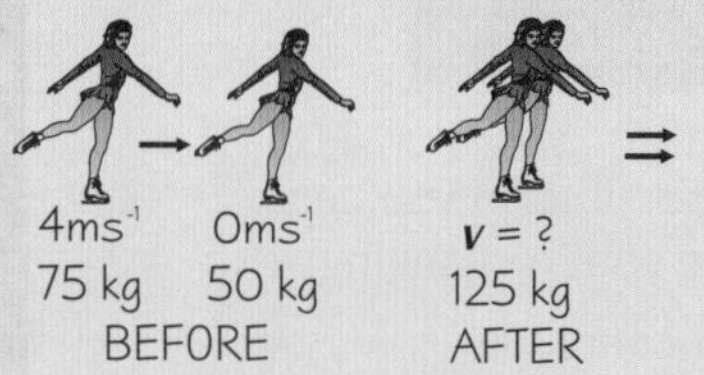

Before you start a momentum calculation, always draw a quick sketch.

Momentum of skaters before = Momentum of skaters after

$$(75 \times 4) + (50 \times 0) = 125v$$
$$300 = 125v$$
$$\text{So } v = 2.4\ ms^{-1}$$

4) The same principle can be applied in **explosions**. E.g. if you fire an **air rifle**, the **forward momentum** gained by the pellet **equals** the **backward momentum** of the rifle, and you feel the rifle recoiling into your shoulder.

Example A bullet of mass 0.005 kg is shot from a rifle at a speed of 200 ms^{-1}. The rifle has a mass of 4 kg. Calculate the velocity at which the rifle recoils.

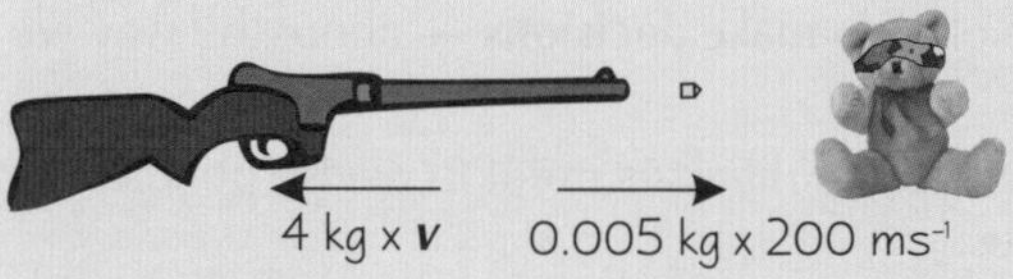

Momentum before explosion = Momentum after explosion

$$0 = (0.005 \times 200) + (4 \times v)$$
$$0 = 1 + 4v$$
$$v = -0.25\ ms^{-1}$$

Rocket Propulsion can be Explained by Momentum

For a **rocket** to be **propelled forward** it must expel **exhaust gases**. The momentum of the rocket in the forward direction is **equal** to the momentum of the exhaust gases in the backward direction.

Example A rocket of mass 500 kg is completely stationary in space, a long way from any gravitational fields. It starts its engines. The rocket ejects 2.0 kg of gas per second at a speed of 1000 ms^{-1}. Calculate the velocity of the rocket after 1 second.
(For the purpose of this calculation ignore the loss of mass due to fuel use.)

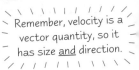

The total momentum before rocket fires = 0 $kg\,ms^{-1}$ as initially the rocket is stationary; the total momentum after rocket fires must also = 0 $kg\,ms^{-1}$.

Total momentum after rocket fires = $(500 \times v) + (2 \times 1000) = 0$

$$500v = -2000$$
$$v = -4\ ms^{-1}$$

The minus sign shows that the rocket moves in the opposite direction to the exhaust gases.

Momentum

Resolve Vectors *to Solve* ***Momentum Calculations*** *in* ***Two Dimensions***

In reality, collisions usually happen in **more than one dimension**. Momentum is still conserved — the only difference is that you have to **resolve the velocity vectors** of the colliding objects to find the components that affect the collision.

Example

A neutron travelling to the right at 5 ms^{-1} collides with a stationary helium nucleus as shown in the diagram. After the collision, the neutron moves in a direction perpendicular to the line of the collision. Draw and label a diagram to show how the particles will move after the impact.

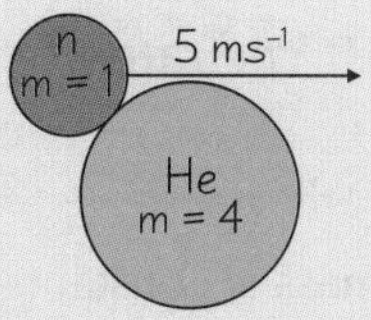

1) Resolve the velocity vector into the components parallel and perpendicular to the line of the collision.

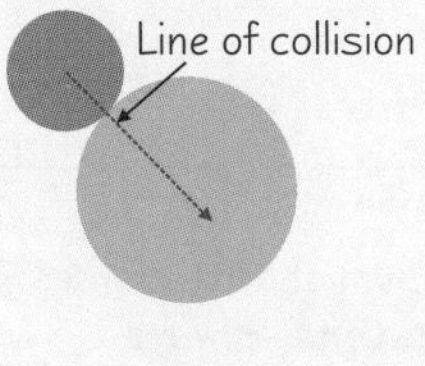

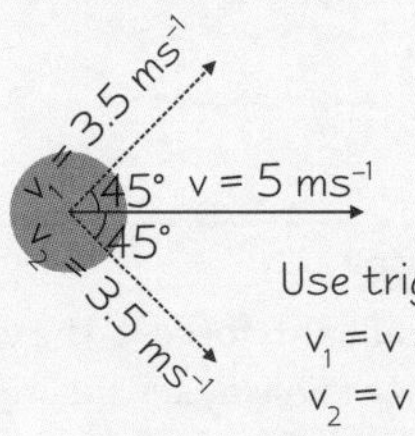

Use trig to resolve:
$v_1 = v \times \cos(45°)$
$v_2 = v \times \sin(45°)$

2) Only the parallel components interact during the collision. The perpendicular components don't change.

3) Then you can ignore v_1 and use v_2 to work out the new velocity of the helium nucleus just like you normally would.

Momentum before = Momentum after
$(1 \times 3.5) + (4 \times 0) = (1 \times 0) + (4 \times \boldsymbol{v})$
$3.5 = 4\boldsymbol{v}$
$\boldsymbol{v} = 0.9\ ms^{-1}$

4) And finally, draw a diagram — remembering to include v_1 and the new velocity vector.

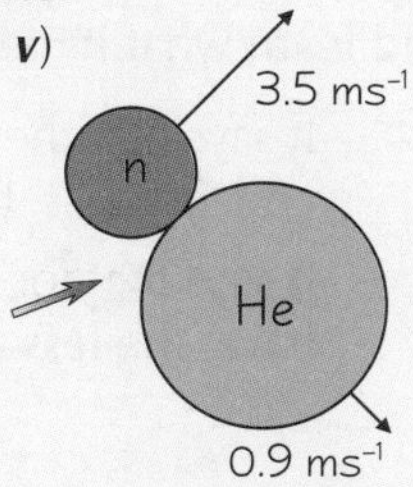

All the momentum calculations you'll encounter in your exam will be in **one or two dimensions** — you don't have to worry about things happening in three dimensions. Remember these four tips for solving problems and you'll be fine:

1) **Sketch a diagram** — things are much easier to understand when you can see exactly what's going on.
2) The **component of the momentum** in the **x-direction** (i.e. across the page) and the component in the **y-direction** (i.e. up and down the page) will **both be conserved** before and after the collision.
3) Only the component of the velocity vector that is **parallel** to the **line of the collision** will have any effect.
4) The component of the velocity vector that is **perpendicular** to the line of the collision will have **no effect**.

Practice Questions

Q1 What is the equation for momentum? What unit is momentum measured in?

Q2 Explain how rocket propulsion is an example of the conservation of momentum.

Q3 Give two other examples of conservation of momentum in practice.

Q4 What do you have to do differently when solving momentum problems in two dimensions?

Exam Questions

Q1 A toy train of mass 0.7 kg, travelling at 0.3 ms^{-1}, collides with a stationary toy carriage of mass 0.4 kg. The two toys couple together. What is their new velocity? [3 marks]

Q2 There are two gliders on an air track. Glider A has a mass of 400 g and is travelling towards Glider B at 4.8 cms^{-1}. Glider B is stationary and has a mass of 200 g. The two gliders collide and join together, moving off at 3.2 cms^{-1}. Show that momentum is conserved in the collision. [2 marks]

Q3 A ball of mass 0.6 kg moving at 5 ms^{-1} collides with a larger stationary ball of mass 2 kg at an angle of 60° to the line of motion, as shown. After the collision, the smaller ball moves in a direction perpendicular to the line of the collision. Draw and label a diagram to show the velocity of the balls immediately after the impact. [5 marks]

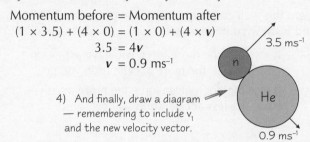

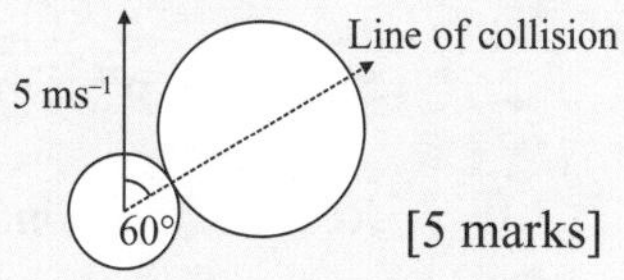

Momentum will never be an endangered species — it's always conserved...

So, guess what — momentum is conserved in collisions. If you forget that you'll really scupper your chances of getting lots of marks from solving momentum problems. So remember, momentum is mass times velocity, and momentum is conserved. See, it's easy — momentum is your friend.

Force and Energy

You did most of this at GCSE, but that doesn't mean you can just skip over it now. You'll be kicking yourself if you forget this stuff in the exam — easy marks...

Newton's 2nd Law says that Force is the Rate of Change of Momentum

*"The **rate of change of momentum** of an object is **directly proportional** to the **resultant force** which acts on the object."* so $F = \frac{\Delta mv}{\Delta t}$

If mass is constant, this can be written as the well-known equation:

resultant force (F) = mass (m) × acceleration (a)

Learn this — it crops up all over the place in A2 Physics.
And learn what it means too:

1) It says that the **more force** you have acting on a certain mass, the **more acceleration** you get.
2) It says that for a given force the **more mass** you have, the **less acceleration** you get.

REMEMBER:
1) The **resultant force** is the **vector sum** of all the forces.
2) The force is **always** measured in **newtons**. **Always**.
3) The **mass** is always measured in **kilograms**.
4) **a** is the **acceleration** of the object as a result of F. It's **always** measured in **metres per second per second** (ms^{-2}).
5) The **acceleration** is always in the **same direction** as the **resultant force**.

Learn the Principle of Conservation of Energy

The **principle of conservation of energy** says that:

Energy **cannot be created** or **destroyed**. Energy **can be transferred** from one form to another but the total amount of energy in a closed system will not change.

Kinetic Energy is the Energy of Anything Moving

As you'll probably remember, **kinetic energy** is the energy of anything **moving** — it depends on the **mass** and **velocity** of whatever is moving. There are two **equations** for kinetic energy that you need to learn — the **standard form** that you'll know and love, and a form written in terms of **momentum**:

$$E_k = \frac{1}{2}mv^2$$

where v is the velocity the object is travelling at and m is its mass.

$$E_k = \frac{p^2}{2m}$$

where p is the momentum of the object and m is its mass.

You need to be able to derive the second form of the equation from the first — don't worry, it's not as scary as it sounds.

1) Start with the equations that you know: $E_k = \frac{1}{2}mv^2$ and $p = mv$.
2) Substitute p for mv in $E_k = \frac{1}{2}mv^2$ to give $E_k = \frac{pv}{2}$.
3) Rearrange $p = mv$ to $v = \frac{p}{m}$.
4) Finally, substitute $\frac{p}{m}$ for v in $E_k = \frac{pv}{2}$ to give $E_k = \frac{p^2}{2m}$.

Simon liked to derive kinetic energy at top speed.

Force and Energy

Kinetic Energy is Conserved in Elastic Collisions

1) As long as there's **no friction**, you know that **momentum is always conserved** in a collision (you have the **same total momentum after** a collision **as you had before**) (see pages 4 and 5).
2) **After** a collision, objects sometimes **stick together**, and sometimes **bounce apart**. Either way the momentum is still **conserved**.
3) But the **kinetic energy** is **not** always conserved. Usually, some of it gets converted into **sound or heat** energy.

In the real world, some energy's <u>always</u> lost in a collision. Sometimes, if the energy loss is small, it's okay to <u>assume</u> the collision is elastic.

A collision where the **total kinetic energy** is the **same** after a collision is called an **elastic collision**.

A collision where the **total kinetic energy** is **less** after a collision is called an **inelastic collision**.

In the diagram on the right, given no friction,

1) it is **always true** that $m_1v_1 + m_2v_2 = m_1v_3 + m_2v_4$
2) it is **sometimes true** that $\frac{1}{2}m_1v_1^2 + \frac{1}{2}m_2v_2^2 = \frac{1}{2}m_1v_3^2 + \frac{1}{2}m_2v_4^2$

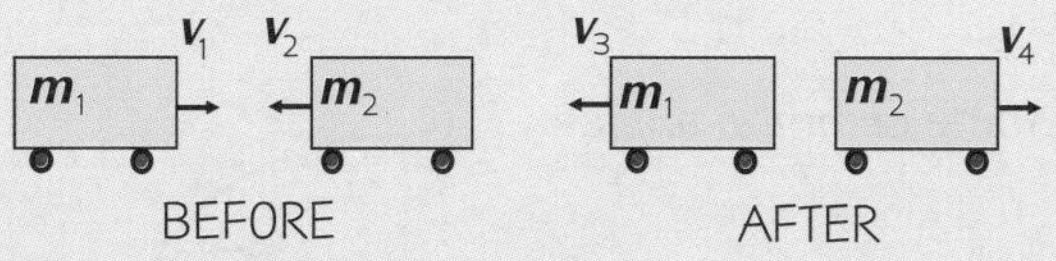

Example

A cart of mass 50 g hurtles at 20 ms^{-1} towards a stationary cart of mass 60 g. After the collision, both carts move forward in the same direction.

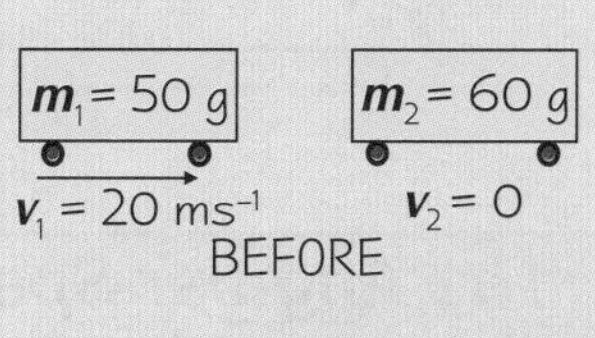

a) If the first cart moves forward at 8 ms^{-1} after the collision, calculate the speed of the second cart.
b) Calculate the total kinetic energy before and after the collision.
c) State whether the collision is elastic or inelastic, giving a reason for your answer.

a) Using conservation of momentum (pages 4–5):
total momentum before = total momentum after
$(0.05 \times 20) + (0.06 \times 0) = (0.05 \times 8) + (0.06 \times v_2)$
$1 = 0.4 + 0.06v_2 \Rightarrow v_2 = 0.6 \div 0.06 =$ **10 ms^{-1}**

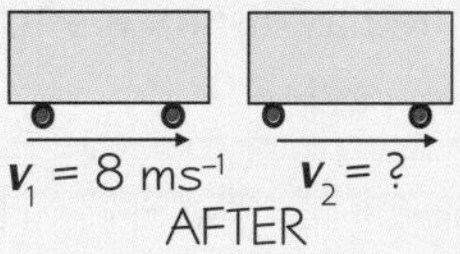

b) kinetic energy = $\frac{1}{2}mv^2$
Before: $KE = \frac{1}{2} \times 0.05 \times 20^2 =$ **10 J**
After: $KE = (\frac{1}{2} \times 0.05 \times 8^2) + (\frac{1}{2} \times 0.06 \times 10^2) = 1.6 + 3 =$ **4.6 J**

c) The collision must be **inelastic**, because the total kinetic energy is reduced in the collision.

Remember — it's not lost, just converted into other forms of energy (heat and sound most likely).

Practice Questions

Q1 State the principle of conservation of energy.

Q2 What are the two equations for calculating kinetic energy?

Q3 What's always conserved in a collision (if there's no friction)?

Q4 What's the difference between elastic and inelastic collisions?

Exam Questions

Q1 A skateboarder is on a half-pipe. He rolls freely down one side of the ramp and up the other. The height of the ramp is 2 m. Take g as 9.81 Nkg^{-1}.

(a) If you assume that there is no friction, what would be his speed at the lowest point of the ramp? [3 marks]

(b) How high will he rise up the other side? [1 mark]

(c) Real ramps are not frictionless, so what must the skater do to reach the top on the other side? [1 mark]

Q2 A railway truck of mass 10 000 kg is travelling at 1 ms^{-1} and collides with a stationary truck of mass 15 000 kg. The two trucks stay together after the collision.

(a) What can you say about the total kinetic energy before and after the collision without calculating anything? [1 mark]

(b) Calculate the final velocity of the two trucks. [2 marks]

(c) Calculate the total kinetic energy before and after the collision. [2 marks]

Want to revise elastic collisions — ping a rubber band at a friend...

As my gran always tells me, 'What you put in is what you get out' — this is a universal truth that works equally well for energy, physics revision and beer. So I guess there's no arguing with me gran (well, her umbrella always deterred me...).

Circular Motion

*It's probably worth putting a bookmark in here — this stuff is needed **all over** the place.*

Angles** can be Expressed in **Radians

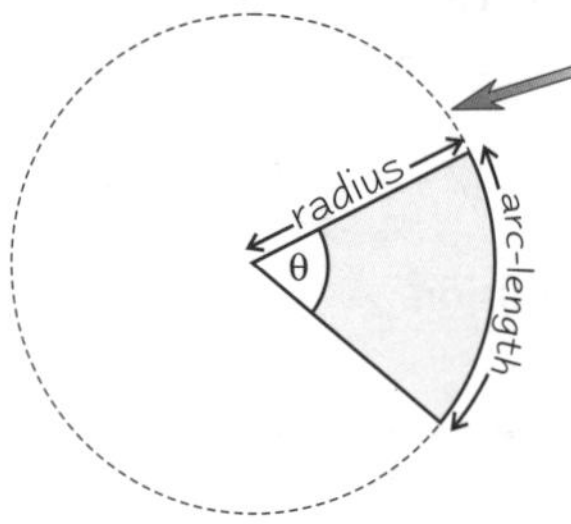

The angle in **radians**, θ, is defined as the **arc-length** divided by the radius of the circle.

For a **complete circle** (360°), the arc-length is just the circumference of the circle ($2\pi r$). Dividing this by the radius (r) gives 2π. So there are 2π radians in a complete circle.

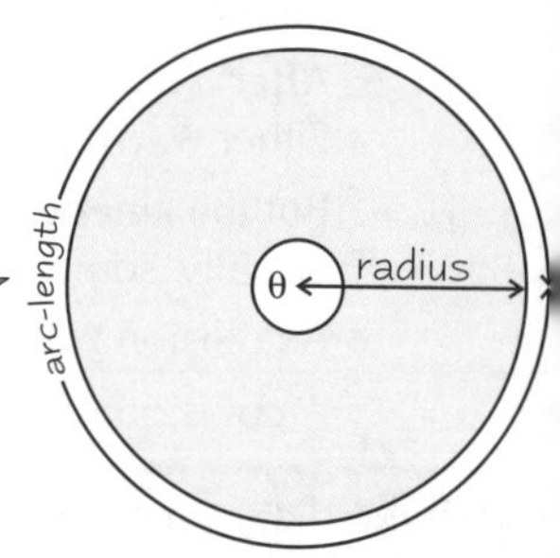

Some common angles:

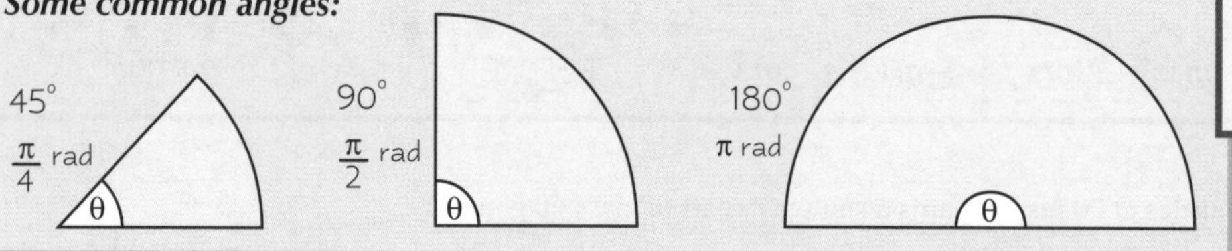

$$\text{angle in radians} = \frac{2\pi}{360} \times \text{angle in degrees}$$

1 radian is about 57°

*The **Angular Speed** is the **Angle** an Object Rotates Through **per Second***

1) Just as **linear speed**, v, is defined as distance ÷ time, the **angular speed**, ω, is defined as **angle ÷ time**. The unit is rad s^{-1} — radians per second.

$$\omega = \frac{\theta}{t}$$

ω = angular speed (rad s^{-1}) — the symbol for angular speed is the little Greek 'omega', not a w.
θ = angle (radians) turned through in a time, t (seconds)

2) The **linear speed**, v, and **angular speed**, ω, of a rotating object are linked by the equation: $v = \omega r$

v = linear speed (ms^{-1}), r = radius of the circle (m), ω = angular speed (rad s^{-1})

Example ***Beam of Particles in a Cyclotron*** (see page 25)

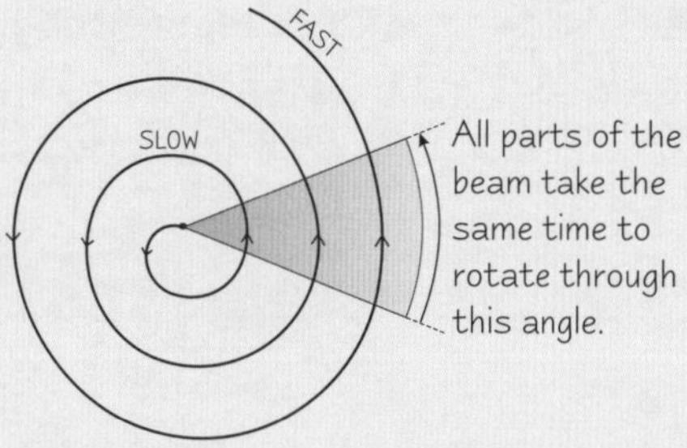

1) Different parts of the particle beam are rotating at **different linear speeds**, v. (The linear speed is sometimes called **tangential velocity**.)
2) But all the parts **rotate** through the **same angle** in the **same time** — so they have the **same angular speed**.

*Circular Motion has a **Frequency** and **Period***

1) The frequency, f, is the number of complete **revolutions per second** (rev s^{-1} or hertz, Hz).
2) The period, T, is the **time taken** for a complete revolution (in seconds).
3) Frequency and period are **linked** by the equation: $f = \frac{1}{T}$ — f = frequency in rev s^{-1}, T = period in s
4) For a complete circle, an object turns through 2π radians in a time T, so frequency and period are related to ω by:

$$\omega = 2\pi f \quad \text{and} \quad T = \frac{2\pi}{\omega}$$

f = frequency in rev s^{-1}, T = period in s, ω = angular speed in rad s^{-1}

Circular Motion

Objects Travelling in Circles are **Accelerating** since their **Velocity is Changing**

1) Even if the car shown is going at a **constant speed**, its **velocity** is changing since its **direction** is changing.
2) Since acceleration is defined as the **rate of change of velocity**, the car is accelerating even though it isn't going any faster.
3) This acceleration is called the **centripetal acceleration** and is always directed towards the **centre of the circle**.

There are two formulas for centripetal acceleration:

$$a = \frac{v^2}{r} \quad \text{and} \quad a = r\omega^2$$

a = centripetal acceleration in ms^{-2}
v = linear speed in ms^{-1}
ω = angular speed in rad s^{-1}
r = radius in m

The **Centripetal Acceleration** is produced by a **Centripetal Force**

From Newton's laws, if there's a **centripetal acceleration**, there must be a **centripetal force** acting towards the **centre of the circle**.

Since $F = ma$, the centripetal force must be:

$$F = \frac{mv^2}{r} \quad \text{and} \quad F = m\omega^2 r$$

The centripetal force is what keeps the object moving in a circle — remove the force and the object would fly off at a tangent.

Men cowered from the force of the centripede.

Practice Questions

Q1 How many radians are there in a complete circle?
Q2 How is angular speed defined and what is the relationship between angular speed and linear speed?
Q3 Define the period and frequency of circular motion. What is the relationship between period and angular speed?
Q4 In which direction does the centripetal force act, and what happens when this force is removed?

Exam Questions

Q1 (a) At what angular speed does the Earth orbit the Sun? (1 year = 3.2×10^7 s) [2 marks]

(b) Calculate the Earth's linear speed. (Assume radius of orbit = 1.5×10^{11} m) [2 marks]

(c) Calculate the centripetal force needed to keep the Earth in its orbit. (Mass of Earth = 6.0×10^{24} kg) [2 marks]

(d) What is providing this force? [1 mark]

Q2 A bucket full of water, tied to a rope, is being swung around in a vertical circle (so it is upside down at the top of the swing). The radius of the circle is 1 m.

(a) By considering the acceleration due to gravity at the top of the swing, what is the minimum frequency with which the bucket can be swung without any water falling out? [3 marks]

(b) The bucket is now swung with a constant angular speed of 5 rad s^{-1}. What will be the tension in the rope when the bucket is at the top of the swing if the total mass of the bucket and water is 10 kg? [2 marks]

I'm spinnin' around, move out of my way...

*"Centripetal" just means "centre-seeking". The centripetal force is what actually causes circular motion. What you **feel** when you're spinning, though, is the reaction (centrifugal) force. Don't get the two mixed up.*

Electric Fields

*Electric fields can be attractive or repulsive. It's all to do with **charge**.*

There is an Electric Field around a Charged Object

Any object with **charge** has an **electric field** around it — the region where it can attract or repel other charges.

1) Electric charge, Q, is measured in **coulombs** (C) and can be either positive or negative.
2) **Oppositely** charged particles **attract** each other. **Like** charges **repel**.
3) If a **charged object** is placed in an electric field, then it will experience a **force**.

You can Calculate Forces using Coulomb's Law

You'll need **Coulomb's law** to work out F — the force of attraction or repulsion between two point charges...

COULOMB'S LAW:

$$F = \frac{kQ_1Q_2}{r^2} \quad \text{where} \quad k = \frac{1}{4\pi\varepsilon}$$

ε ("epsilon") = permittivity of material between charges
Q_1 and Q_2 are the charges
r is the distance between Q_1 and Q_2

If the charges are **opposite** then the force is **attractive**. F will be **negative**.

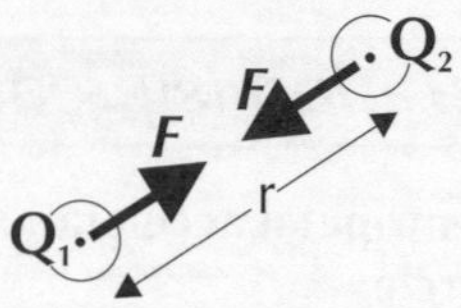

If Q_1 and Q_2 are **like** charges then the force is **repulsive**, and F will be **positive**.

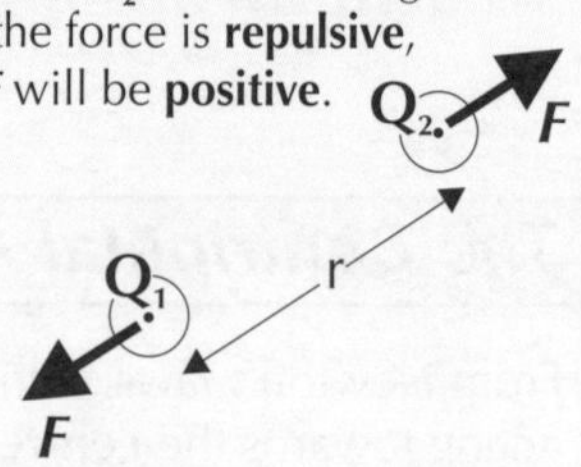

1) The force on Q_1 is always **equal** and **opposite** to the force on Q_2.
2) It's an **inverse square law**. The further apart the charges are, the weaker the force between them.
3) The size of the force F also depends on the **permittivity**, ε, of the material between the two charges. For free space, the permittivity is $\varepsilon_0 = 8.85 \times 10^{-12}\ C^2N^{-1}m^{-2}$.

Electric Fields can be Radial or Uniform

Electric fields can be represented by **field lines**. The lines show the **shape** and **direction** of the field.

1) A **point charge**, or any body that behaves as if all its charge is concentrated at the centre, has a **radial** field.

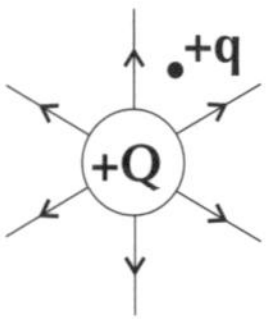

For a **positive *Q***, a small positive 'test' charge ***q*** would be **repelled**, so the field lines point **away** from ***Q***.

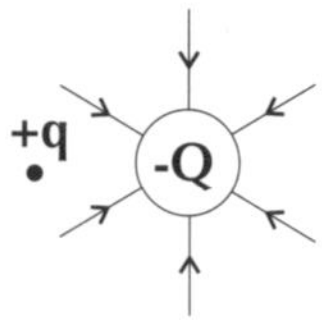

For a **negative *Q***, a small positive charge ***q*** would be **attracted**, so the field lines point **towards *Q***.

2) A **uniform field** can be produced by connecting two **parallel plates** to the opposite poles of a battery.

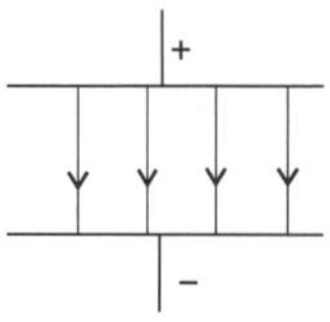

The **field lines** are **parallel** to each other and point **from** the **positive** plate **towards** the **negative** plate.

Electric Field Strength is Force per Unit Charge

Electric field strength, E, is defined as the **force per unit positive charge** — the force that a charge of +1 C would experience if it was placed in the electric field.

$$E = \frac{F}{Q}$$

F is the force on a charge Q

1) E is a **vector** pointing in the **direction** that a **positive charge** would **move**.
2) The units of E are **newtons per coulomb** (NC^{-1}).
3) You can think of **field strength** as a measure of how **tightly packed** the **field lines** are.
4) In a **radial field**, the field strength depends on **how far you are** from the charge.
5) In a **uniform field**, the field strength is the **same everywhere**.

Electric Fields

In a Radial Field, E is Inversely Proportional to r^2

1) As you go **further away** from a point charge ***Q***, the **field lines** get **further apart** and the field strength **decreases**.
2) To calculate the **field strength** at a distance ***r*** from a charge **Q** you need to combine the two equations on page 10.

1) Write equations for the force and electric field strength for a point charge ***q*** placed at a distance ***r*** from ***Q***. $F = \frac{kQq}{r^2}$ $E = \frac{F}{q}$

2) Substitute $F = \frac{kQq}{r^2}$ in $E = \frac{F}{q}$ to give $E = \frac{kQq}{qr^2}$.

3) Cancel ***q*** from the top and bottom of the fraction to leave $E = \frac{kQ}{r^2}$ where $k = \frac{1}{4\pi\varepsilon}$

In a Uniform Field, E is the Same Everywhere

In a **uniform field**, the field lines are **parallel** so they're always the **same distance** apart. This means that the field strength is the **same at all points** within the field — i.e. a test charge would experience the **same force** wherever it was.

The **field strength** between two **parallel plates** depends on the **potential difference**, ***V***, and the **distance**, ***d***, between them, according to the equation:

$$E = \frac{V}{d}$$

E can be measured in volts per metre (Vm^{-1})

Investigating a Uniform Field

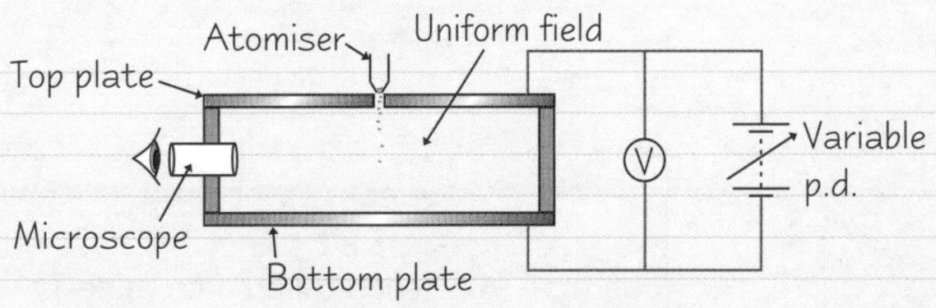

1) An **atomiser** creates a **fine mist** of oil drops that are **charged** by **friction** as they leave the atomiser.
2) When the circuit is **off**, the drops **fall** from the top plate to the bottom plate due to their **weight**.
3) When the circuit is **switched on**, the potential difference between the plates creates a **uniform electric field**, which exerts a **force** on the oil drops. A negatively charged oil drop can be made to '**float**' between the plates by **balancing** the **upward force** from the electric field with the **downward force** of the oil drop's weight.
4) If you **increase the p.d.**, you **increase the field strength** so the **oil drop** moves towards the **positive top plate**.
5) If you **increase the distance** between the plates or **decrease the p.d.**, you **reduce the field strength** and the oil drop falls to the bottom plate due to its weight.

Practice Questions

Q1 Draw the electric field lines due to a positive charge, and due to a negative charge.

Q2 Write down Coulomb's law.

Exam Questions

Q1 The diagram shows two electric charges with equal but opposite charge. $Q = 1.6 \times 10^{-19}$ C.

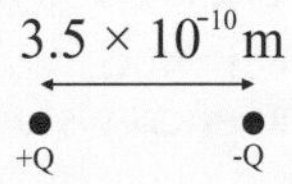

(a) Draw electric field lines to show the electric field in the area surrounding the charges. [3 marks]

(b) The distance between the charges is 3.5×10^{-10} m. Find the strength of the electric field halfway between the charges. [3 marks]

Q2 (a) Two parallel plates are separated by an air gap of 4.5 mm. The plates are connected to a 1500 V dc supply. What is the electric field strength between the plates? Give a suitable unit and state the direction of the field. [3 marks]

(b) The plates are now pulled further apart so that the distance between them is doubled. The electric field strength remains the same. What is the new voltage between the plates? [2 marks]

Electric fields — one way to roast beef...

At least you get a choice here — uniform or radial, positive or negative, attractive or repulsive, chocolate or strawberry...

Capacitors

Capacitors are things that store electrical charge — like a charge bucket. The capacitance of one of these things tells you how much charge the bucket can hold. Sounds simple enough... ha... ha, ha, ha...

Capacitance is Defined as the Amount of **Charge Stored** per **Volt**

$$C = \frac{Q}{V}$$

where Q is the **charge** in coulombs, V is the **potential difference** in volts and C is the **capacitance** in farads (F) — **1 farad = 1 C V^{-1}**.

A farad is a **huge** unit so you'll usually see capacitances expressed in terms of:

μF — microfarads ($\times 10^{-6}$)
nF — nanofarads ($\times 10^{-9}$)
pF — picofarads ($\times 10^{-12}$)

You can **Investigate** the **Charge Stored** by a **Capacitor Experimentally**

Investigating the Charge Stored on a Capacitor

1) Set up a **test circuit** to measure current and potential difference:

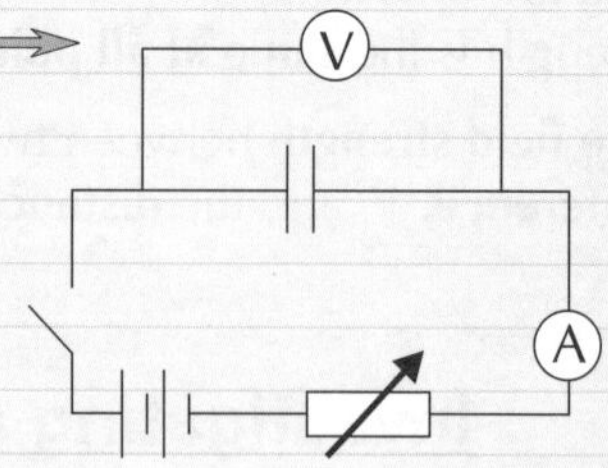

2) Constantly adjust the **variable resistor** to keep the charging current **constant** for as long as you can (it's impossible when the capacitor is nearly fully charged).
3) Record the p.d. at regular intervals until it **equals** the **battery p.d.**
4) From these results, you can plot the following graphs:

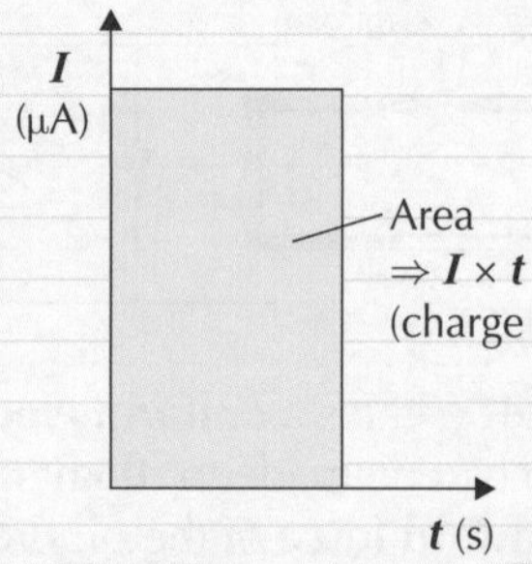

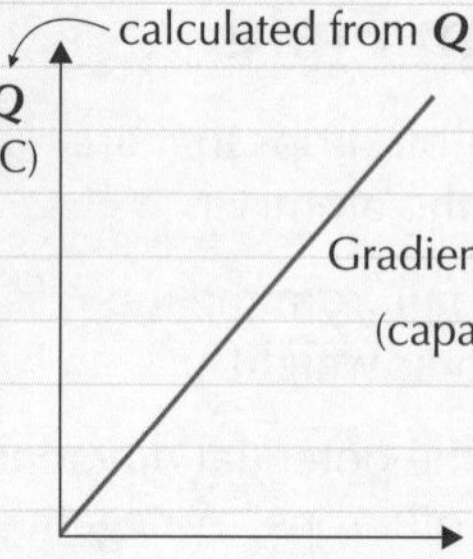

Capacitors **Store Energy**

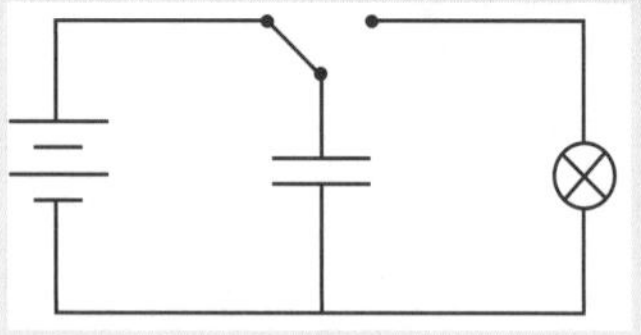

1) In this circuit, when the switch is flicked to the **left**, **charge** builds up on the plates of the **capacitor**. **Electrical energy**, provided by the battery, is **stored** by the capacitor.
2) If the switch is flicked to the **right**, the energy stored on the plates will **discharge** through the **bulb**, converting electrical energy into light and heat.
3) **Work** is done **removing charge** from **one plate** and depositing **opposite charge** onto the other one. The energy for this must come from the **electrical energy** of the **battery**, and is given by **charge × p.d.** The energy **stored** by a capacitor is **equal** to the **work done** by the **battery**.
4) So, you can find the **energy stored** by the capacitor from the **area** under a **graph** of **p.d.** against **charge stored** on the capacitor.
The p.d. across the capacitor is **proportional** to the charge stored on it, so the graph will be a **straight line** through the origin.
The **energy stored** is given by the **yellow triangle**.

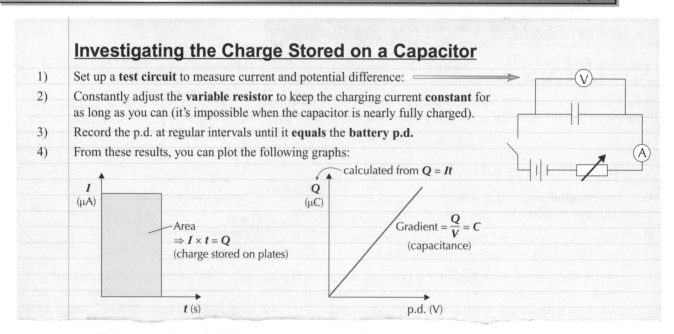

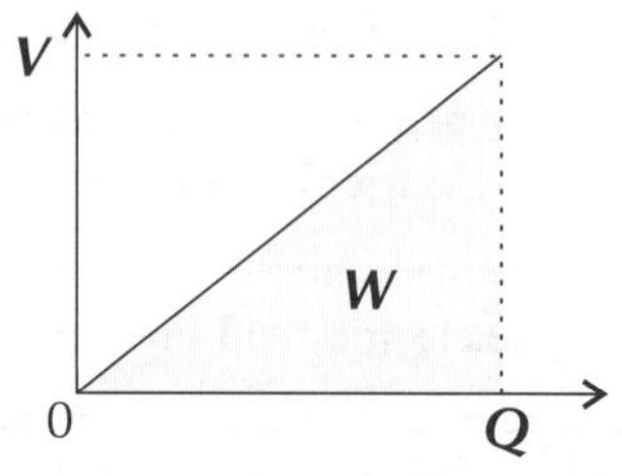

5) **Area of triangle = ½ × base × height**, so the energy stored by the capacitor is:

$$W = \frac{1}{2}QV$$

W stands for 'work done', but you can also use *E* for energy

Capacitors

There are **Three** Expressions for the **Energy Stored** by a Capacitor

1) You know the first one already: $W = \frac{1}{2}QV$

2) $C = \frac{Q}{V}$, so $Q = CV$. Substitute that into the energy equation: $W = \frac{1}{2}CV \times V$. So: $W = \frac{1}{2}CV^2$

3) $V = \frac{Q}{C}$, so $W = \frac{1}{2}Q \times \frac{Q}{C}$. Simplify: $W = \frac{Q^2}{2C}$

Example *A 900 μF capacitor is charged up to a potential difference of 240 V. Calculate the energy stored by the capacitor.*

First, choose the best equation to use — you've been given **V** and **C**, so you need $W = \frac{1}{2}CV^2$.

Substitute the values in: $W = \frac{1}{2} \times 9 \times 10^{-4} \times 240^2 = 25.92$ J

Practice Questions

Q1 Define capacitance.

Q2 What is the relationship between charge, voltage and capacitance?

Q3 Write the following in standard form: a) 220 μF b) 1000 pF c) 470 nF.

Q4 State two different equations for the charge stored by a capacitor.

Exam Questions

Q1 The graphs show charge stored by a capacitor against the potential difference across it, and the current used to charge the capacitor.

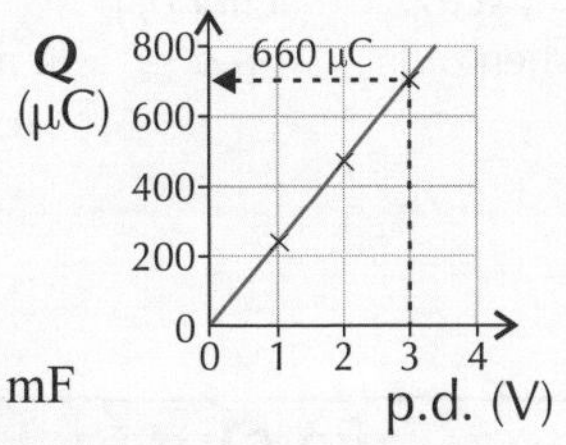

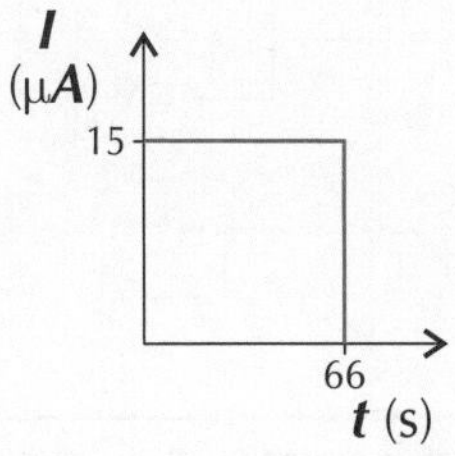

(a) The capacitance of the capacitor is:
A 198 μF **B** 220 μF **C** 1980 μF **D** 220 mF [1 mark]

(b) The charge stored on the plates of the capacitor is:
A 110 μC **B** 440 μC **C** 495 μC **D** 990 μC [1 mark]

Q2 A 500 mF capacitor is fully charged up from a 12 V supply.

(a) Calculate the total energy stored by the capacitor. [2 marks]

(b) Calculate the charge stored by the capacitor. [2 marks]

Q3 A battery is used to charge a 470 μF capacitor. When the capacitor is fully charged, it stores 4.23 mC of charge.

(a) Show that the energy stored by the capacitor is approximately 0.02 J. [2 marks]

(b) Calculate the voltage of the battery. [2 marks]

Capacitance — fun, it's not...

Capacitors are really useful in the real world. Pick an appliance, any appliance, and it'll probably have a capacitor or several. If I'm being honest, though, the only saving grace of these pages for me is that they're not especially hard...

Charging and Discharging

Charging and discharging — sounds painful...

You can **Charge** a **Capacitor** by Connecting it to a **Battery**

1) When a capacitor is connected to a **battery**, a **current** flows in the circuit until the capacitor is **fully charged**, then **stops**.

2) The electrons flow onto the plate connected to the **negative terminal** of the battery, so a **negative charge** builds up.

3) This build-up of negative charge **repels** electrons off the plate connected to the **positive terminal** of the battery, making that plate positive. These electrons are attracted to the positive terminal of the battery.

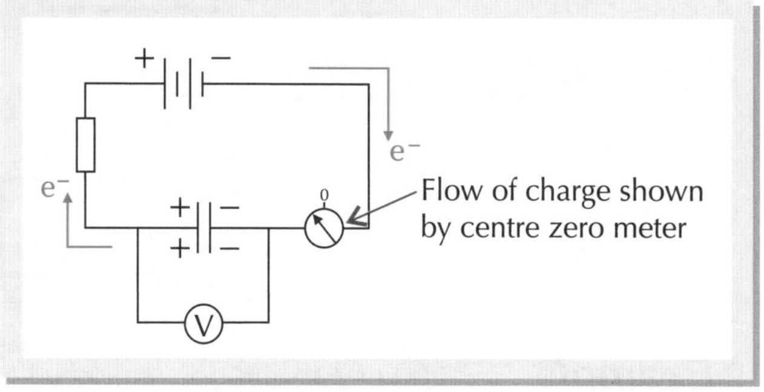

4) An **equal** but **opposite** charge builds up on each plate, causing a **potential difference** between the plates. Remember that **no charge** can flow **between** the plates because they're **separated** by an **insulator** (dielectric).

5) Initially the **current** through the circuit is **high**. But, as **charge** builds up on the plates, **electrostatic repulsion** makes it **harder** and **harder** for more electrons to be deposited. When the p.d. across the **capacitor** is equal to the p.d. across the **battery**, the **current** falls to **zero**. The capacitor is **fully charged**.

an equal but opposite charge

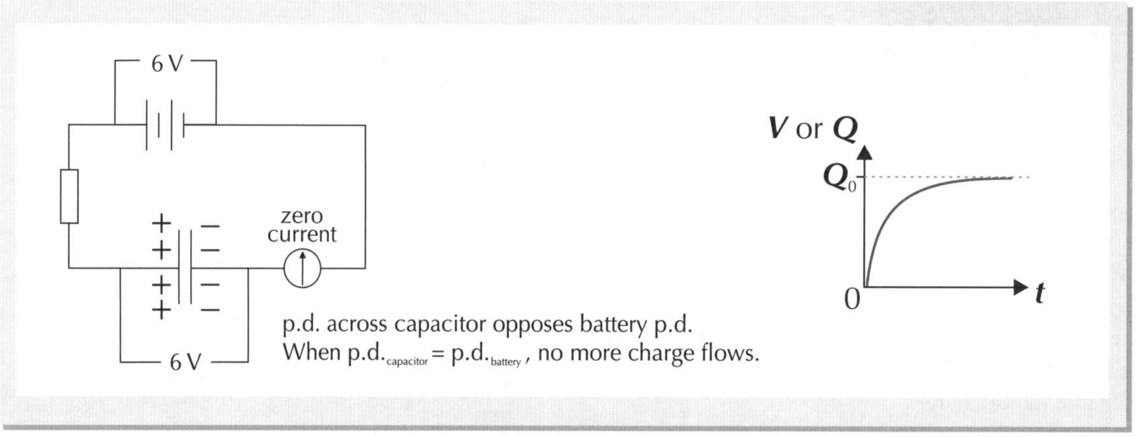

To **Discharge** a Capacitor, **Take Out** the **Battery** and **Reconnect** the **Circuit**

1) When a **charged capacitor** is connected across a **resistor**, the p.d. drives a **current** through the circuit.
2) This current flows in the **opposite direction** from the **charging current**.
3) The capacitor is **fully discharged** when the **p.d.** across the plates and the **current** in the circuit are both **zero**.

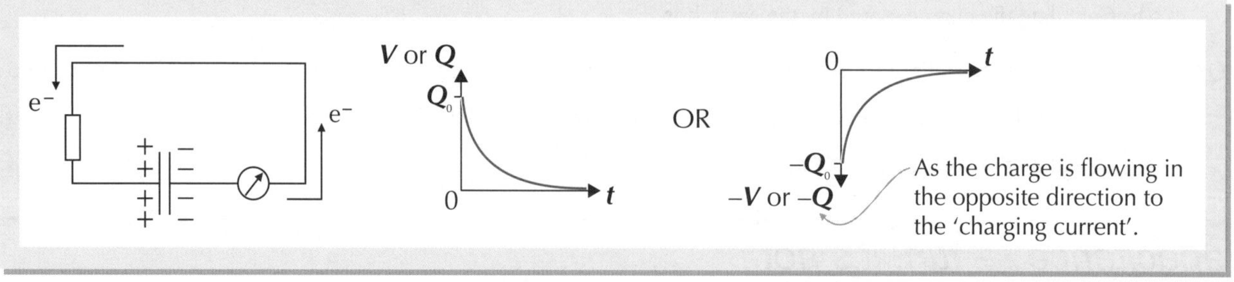

Charging and Discharging

The **Time Taken** to **Charge** or **Discharge** Depends on **Two Factors**

The **time** it takes to charge up or discharge a capacitor depends on:

1) The **capacitance** of the capacitor (*C*). This affects the amount of **charge** that can be transferred at a given **voltage**.
2) The **resistance** of the circuit (***R***). This affects the **current** in the circuit.

The **Charge** on a Capacitor **Decreases Exponentially**

1) When a capacitor is **discharging**, the amount of **charge** left on the plates falls **exponentially with time**.
2) That means it always takes the **same length of time** for the charge to **halve**, no matter **how much charge** you start with — like radioactive decay (see p. 42).

The charge left on the plates of a capacitor discharging from full is given by the equation:

$$Q = Q_0 e^{-\frac{t}{RC}}$$

where Q_0 is the charge of the capacitor when it's fully charged.

The graphs of V against t and I against t for charging and discharging are also exponential.

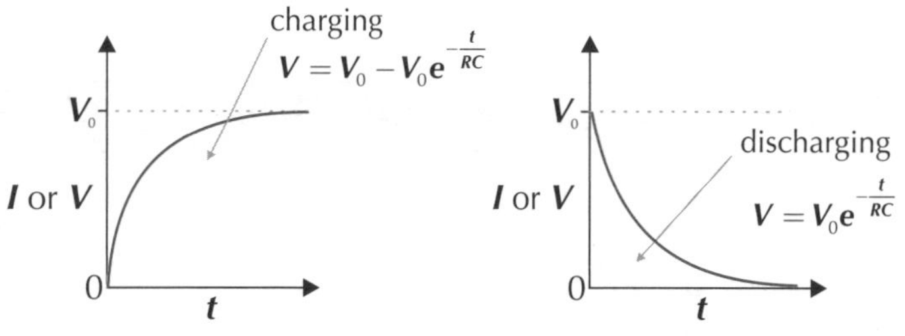

Time Constant τ = RC

τ is the Greek letter 'tau'

If $t = \tau = RC$ is put into the equation above, then $Q = Q_0 e^{-1}$. So when $t = \tau$: $\frac{Q}{Q_0} = \frac{1}{e}$, where $\frac{1}{e} \approx \frac{1}{2.718} \approx 0.37$.

1) So τ, the **time constant**, is the time taken for the charge on a discharging capacitor (Q) to **fall** to **37%** of Q_0.
2) It's also the time taken for the charge of a charging capacitor to **rise** to **63%** of Q_0.
3) The **larger** the **resistance** in series with the capacitor, the **longer it takes** to charge or discharge.
4) In practice, the time taken for a capacitor to charge or discharge **fully** is taken to be about 5***RC***.

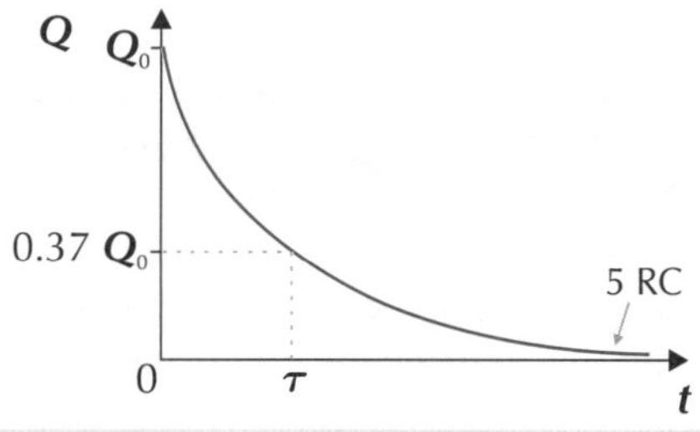

Practice Questions

Q1 Sketch graphs to show the variation of p.d. across the plates of a capacitor with time for:
a) charging a capacitor, b) discharging a capacitor.

Q2 What two factors affect the rate of charge of a capacitor?

Exam Question

Q1 A 250 μF capacitor is fully charged from a 6 V battery and then discharged through a 1 kΩ resistor.

(a) Calculate the time taken for the charge on the capacitor to fall to 37% of its original value. [2 marks]

(b) Calculate the percentage of the total charge remaining on the capacitor after 0.7s. [3 marks]

(c) If the charging voltage is increased to 12 V, what effect will this have on:

i) the total charge stored, ii) the capacitance of the capacitor, iii) the time taken to fully charge [3 marks]

An analogy — consider the lowly bike pump...

One way to think of the charging process is like pumping air into a bike tyre. To start with, the air goes in easily, but as the tyre pressure increases, it gets harder and harder to squeeze more air in. The analogy works just as well for discharging...

Magnetic Fields and Forces

Magnetic fields — making pretty patterns with iron filings before spending an age trying to pick them off the magnet.

A **Magnetic Field** is a **Region** Where a **Force** is Exerted on **Magnetic Materials**

Magnetic fields can be represented by **field lines**. Field lines go from **north to south**.
Just as with electric fields (see page 10), the **closer** together the lines, the **stronger** the field.

The **field lines** around a **bar magnet**, or pair of magnets, have a characteristic shape:

At a neutral point magnetic fields cancel out.

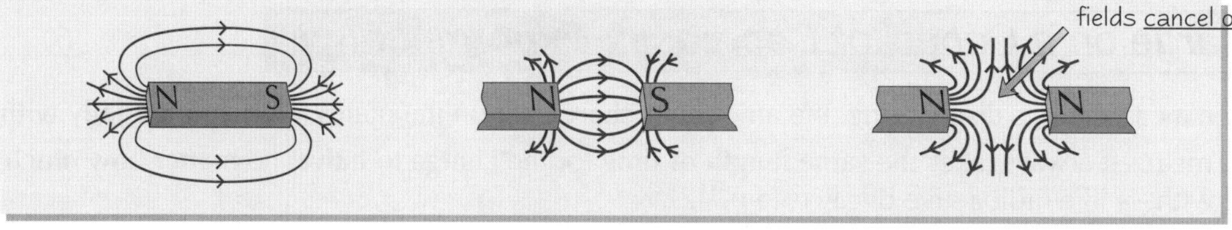

There is a **Magnetic Field** Around a **Wire** Carrying **Electric Current**

1) The **direction** of a magnetic **field** around a current-carrying wire can be worked out with the **right-hand rule**.
2) You also need to learn these diagrams for a **single coil** and a **solenoid**:

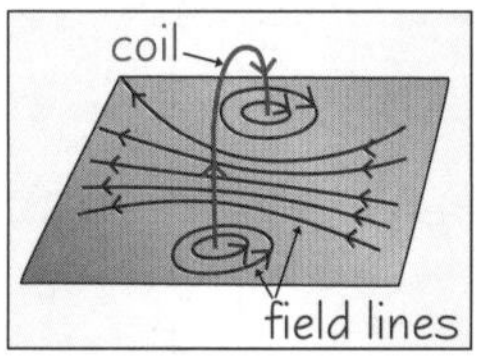

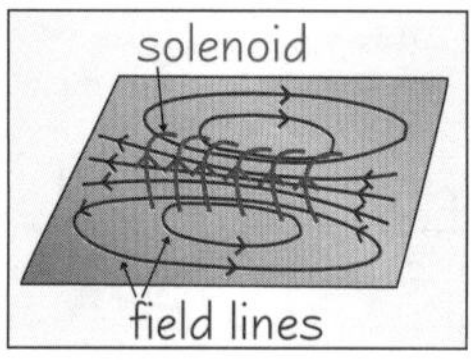

RIGHT-HAND RULE

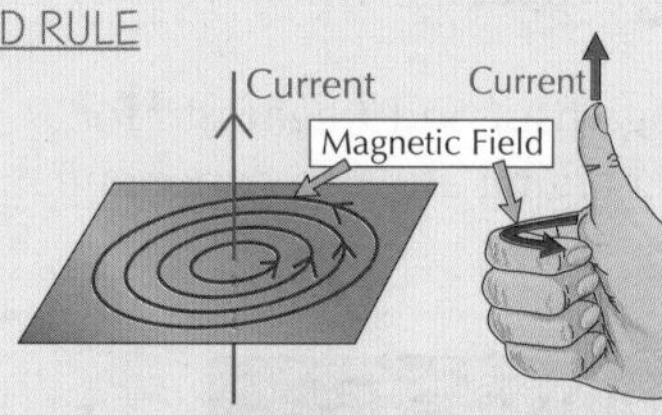

1) Stick your right thumb up, like you're hitching a lift.
2) If your thumb points in the direction of the current...
3) ...your curled fingers point in the direction of the field.

Think of the **Magnetic Flux** as the Total **Number** of **Field Lines**...

1) **Magnetic field strength**, or **magnetic flux density**, ***B***, is a measure of the **strength** of the magnetic field **per unit area**. It's a vector quantity with both a **direction** and **magnitude**, and is measured in **teslas, T**.
2) The total **magnetic flux**, ϕ, passing through an **area**, ***A***, perpendicular to a **magnetic field**, ***B***, is defined as:

$$\phi = BA$$

3) When you move a **coil** in a magnetic field, the size of the **e.m.f.** induced (see p.19) depends on the **magnetic flux**, ϕ, and the **number of turns** on the coil.
The product of these is called the **flux linkage**, Φ.
For a coil of ***N*** turns perpendicular to ***B***, the flux linkage is given by:

$$\Phi = N\phi = BAN$$

ϕ is the little Greek letter 'phi', and Φ is a capital 'phi'.

4) The unit of both ϕ and Φ is the **weber, Wb**.

A change in flux of one weber per second will induce an electromotive force of 1 volt in a loop of wire.

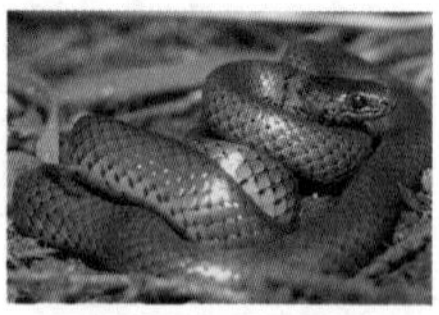

Nige was understandably proud the day he beat his N = 3 record.

Example

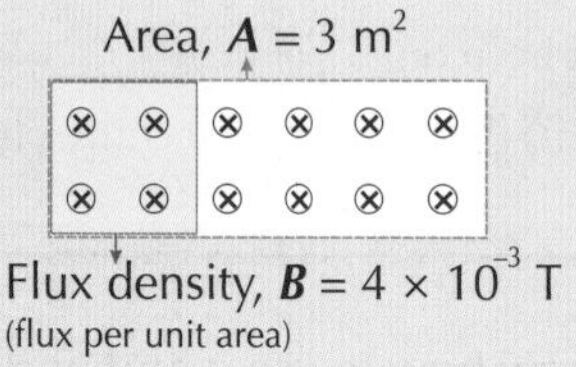

$\phi = BA = 4 \times 10^{-3} \times 3 = 1.2 \times 10^{-2}$ Wb

If this is the magnetic flux inside a solenoid of 10 turns, the flux linkage will be $\Phi = N\phi = 0.12$ Wb

Magnetic Fields and Forces

A Wire Carrying a Current in a Magnetic Field will Experience a Force

1) A **force acts** if a current-carrying wire **cuts magnetic flux** lines.
2) If the current is **parallel** to the flux lines, **no force** acts.
3) The **direction** of the force is always **perpendicular** to both the **current** direction and the **magnetic field**.
4) The direction of the force is given by **Fleming's Left-Hand Rule.**

Fleming's Left-Hand Rule

The First finger points in the direction of the uniform magnetic Field, the seCond finger points in the direction of the conventional Current. Then your thuMb points in the direction of the force (in which Motion takes place).

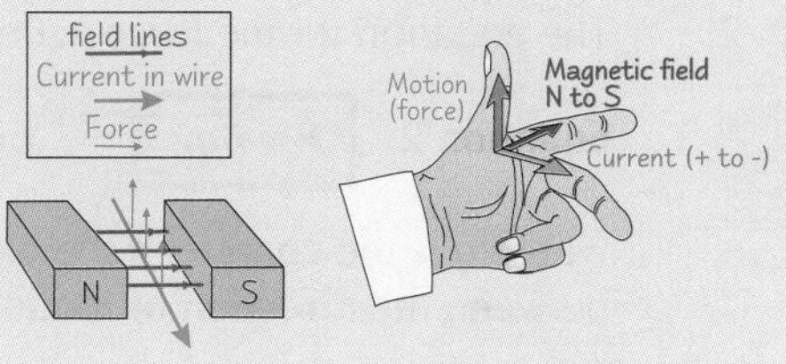

The Size of the Force can be Calculated...

1) The size of the **force**, ***F***, on a current-carrying wire at right angles to a magnetic field is proportional to the **current**, ***I***, the **length of wire** in the field, ***l***, and the **strength of the magnetic field**, ***B***. This gives the equation:

$$F = BIl$$

2) In this equation, the **magnetic field strength**, ***B***, is defined as:

The force on one metre of wire carrying a current of one amp at right angles to the magnetic field.

You can think of the magnetic field strength as the number of flux lines per unit area (see previous page).

The Force is Greatest when the Wire and Field are Perpendicular...

1) The **force** on a current-carrying wire in a magnetic field is caused by the **component** of field strength which is **perpendicular** to the wire — $B \sin \theta$.
2) So, for a wire at an **angle** θ to the field, the **force** acting on the wire is given by:

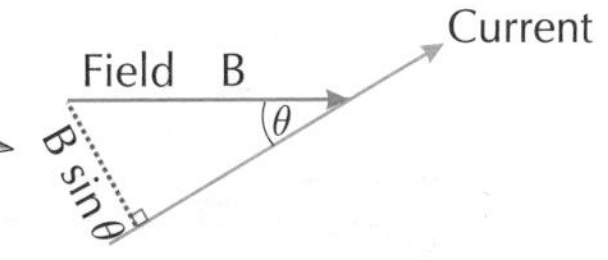

$$F = BIl \sin \theta$$

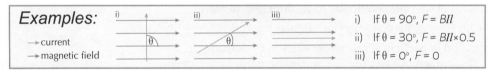

Examples:

→current
→magnetic field

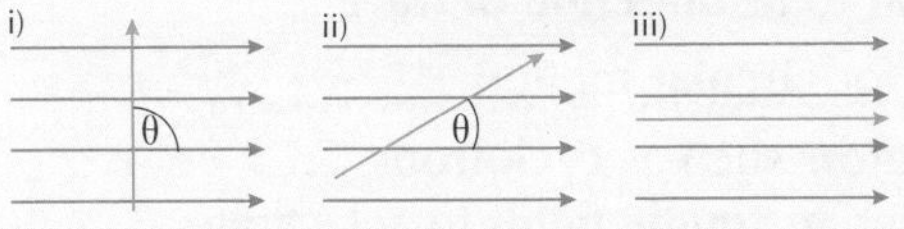

i) If $\theta = 90°$, $F = BIl$
ii) If $\theta = 30°$, $F = BIl \times 0.5$
iii) If $\theta = 0°$, $F = 0$

Practice Questions

Q1 Describe why a current-carrying wire at right angles to an external magnetic field will experience a force.

Q2 Sketch the magnetic fields around a long straight current-carrying wire, and a solenoid. Show the direction of the current and magnetic field on each diagram.

Q3 A copper bar can roll freely on two copper supports, as shown in the diagram. When current is applied in the direction shown, which way will the bar roll?

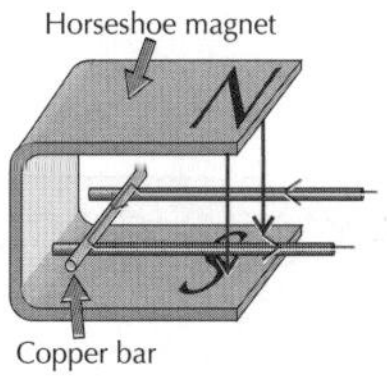

Exam Question

Q1 A wire carrying a current of 3 A runs perpendicular to a magnetic field of strength 2×10^{-5} T. 4 cm of the wire is within the field.

(a) Calculate the magnitude of the force on the wire. [2 marks]

(b) If the wire is rotated so that it is at 30° to the field, what would the size of the force be? [2 marks]

I revised the right-hand rule by the A69 and ended up in Newcastle...

Fleming's left-hand rule is the key to this section — so make sure you know how to use it and understand what it all means. Remember that the direction of the magnetic field is from N to S, and that the current is from +ve to –ve — this is as important as using the correct hand. You need to get those right or it'll all go to pot...

Charged Particles in Magnetic Fields

Magnetic fields are used a lot when dealing with particle beams — you'll be learning more about their uses in Unit 5.

Forces Act on Charged Particles in Magnetic Fields

Electric current in a wire is caused by the **flow** of negatively **charged** electrons. These charged particles are affected by **magnetic fields** — so a current-carrying wire **experiences a force** in a magnetic field (see pages 16–17).

1) The equation for the **force** exerted on a **current-carrying wire** in a **magnetic field** perpendicular to the current is: **Equation 1:** $F = BIl$

You met this equation on the previous page.

2) The equation for the **force** acting on a **single charged particle moving perpendicular to a magnetic field** is:

Equation 2: $F = Bqv$ or, more generally **Equation 3:** $F = Bqv \sin\theta$

where q is the **charge** on the particle, v is its **velocity** and θ is the **angle** between the **direction of motion** and the **magnetic field**.

In many exam questions, q is the size of the charge on the electron, which is 1.6×10^{-19} coulombs.

Example

An electron is travelling at 2×10^4 ms^{-1} through a uniform magnetic field of strength 2 T.
Find the force on the electron when: a) it is travelling at right angles to the magnetic field.
b) it is travelling at 30° to the direction of the magnetic field.
(The magnitude of the charge on an electron is 1.6×10^{-19} C.)

a) $F = Bqv$
so, $F = 2 \times 1.6 \times 10^{-19} \times 2 \times 10^4$
so, $F = 6.4 \times 10^{-15}$ N

b) $F = Bqv \sin\theta$
so, $F = 2 \times 1.6 \times 10^{-19} \times 2 \times 10^4 \times \sin 30°$
so, $F = 6.4 \times 10^{-15} \times 0.5$
so, $F = 3.2 \times 10^{-15}$ N

Charged Particles in a Magnetic Field are Deflected in a Circular Path

1) By **Fleming's left-hand rule** the force on a **moving charge** in a magnetic field is always **perpendicular** to its **direction of travel**.
2) Mathematically, that is the condition for **circular** motion.
3) This effect is used in **particle accelerators** such as **cyclotrons** (see page 25) — which use **electric** and **magnetic fields** to accelerate particles to very **high energies** along circular paths.
4) The **radius of curvature** of the **path** of a charged particle moving through a magnetic field gives you information about the particle's **charge** and **mass** — this means you can **identify different particles** by studying how they're **deflected** (see pages 33-35).

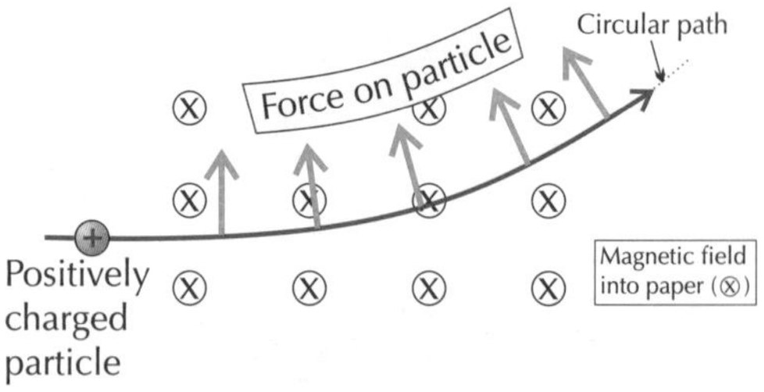

Charges Accumulate on a Conductor Moving Through a Magnetic Field

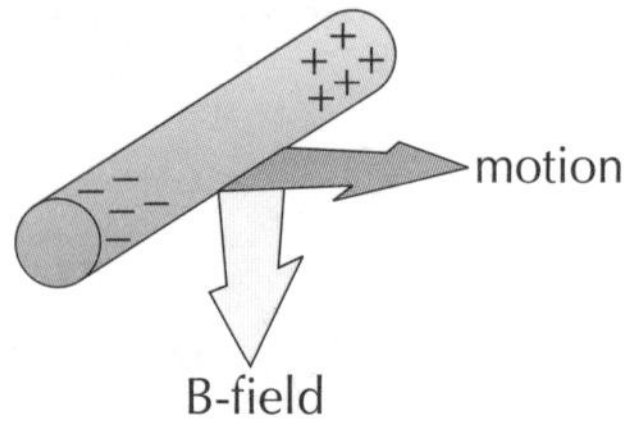

1) If a **conducting rod** moves through a magnetic field its **electrons** will experience a **force**, which means that they will **accumulate** at one end of the rod.
2) This **induces** an **e.m.f.** (**electromotive force**) across the ends of the rod exactly as a **battery** would.
3) If the rod is part of a complete **circuit**, then an induced **current** will **flow** through it — this is called **electromagnetic induction**.
4) An **e.m.f.** is **induced** whenever there is **relative motion** between a **conductor** and a **magnet**.
5) The **conductor** can **move** and the **magnetic field** stay **still** or the **other way round** — you get an e.m.f. either way.
6) An **e.m.f.** is **produced** whenever **lines of force** (flux) are **cut**.
7) **Flux cutting** always induces e.m.f. but will only **induce** a **current** if the **circuit** is complete.

Charged Particles in Magnetic Fields

E.m.f. is Proportional to Rate of Change of Flux Linkage

FARADAY'S LAW: The **induced e.m.f.** is **directly proportional** to the **rate of change of flux linkage**.

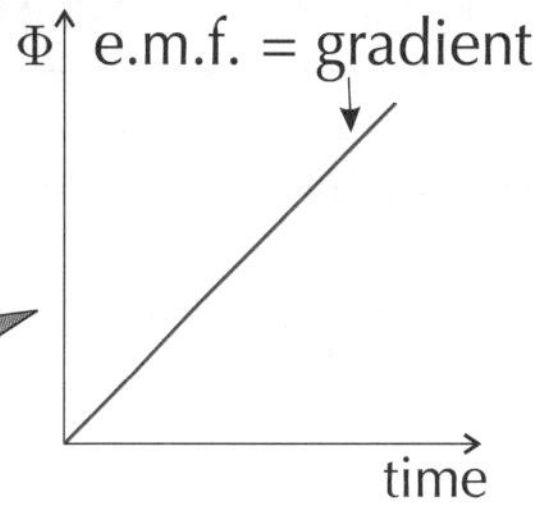

1) **Faraday's Law** can be written as:

$$\text{Induced e.m.f.} = \frac{\text{flux change}}{\text{time taken}} = \frac{d\Phi}{dt} = \frac{d(N\phi)}{dt}$$

2) The **size** of the e.m.f. is shown by the **gradient** of a graph of **Φ** against time.

3) The **area under** the graph of e.m.f. against time gives the **flux change**.

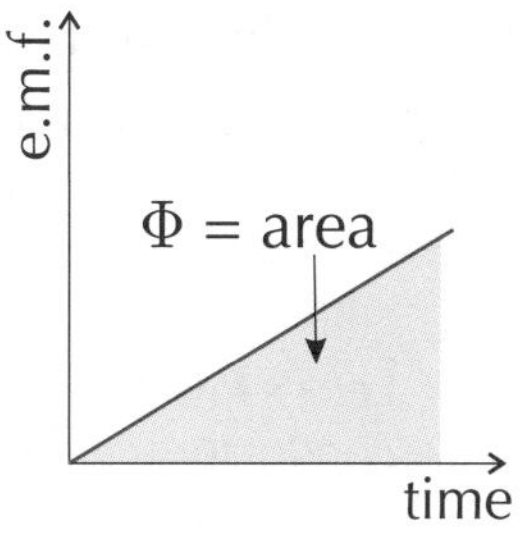

Example

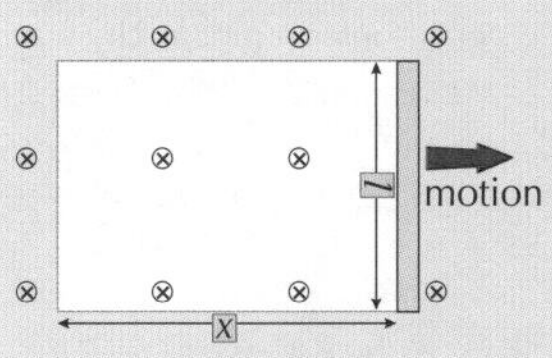

A conducting rod of **length *l*** moves a **distance *x*** through a perpendicular magnetic field.

a) What is the flux cut by the rod in terms of ***l*** and ***x***?
$\phi = BA = Blx$

b) What is the induced e.m.f. in the rod, in terms of the rod's velocity, ***v***?

$$\text{Induced e.m.f.} = \frac{\text{flux change}}{\text{time taken}} = \frac{Blx}{t} = Blv$$

(since $v = x \div t$)

Exam questions often ask you to calculate the e.m.f. induced by the Earth's magnetic field across the wingspan of a plane. Think of it as a moving rod and use the equation above.

Practice Questions

Q1 What is the difference between magnetic flux density, magnetic flux and magnetic flux linkage?

Q2 What is needed for flux cutting to induce a current?

Q3 State Faraday's law.

Q4 Explain how you can find the direction of an induced e.m.f. in a copper bar moving at right angles to a magnetic field.

Exam Questions

Q1 (a) What is the force on an electron travelling at a velocity of 5×10^6 ms^{-1} through a perpendicular magnetic field of 0.77 T? [The charge on an electron is -1.6×10^{-19} C.] [2 marks]

(b) Explain why it follows a circular path while in the field. [1 mark]

Q2 A coil of area 0.23 m^2 is placed at right angles to a magnetic field of 2×10^{-3} T.

(a) What is the magnetic flux passing through the coil? [2 marks]

(b) If the coil has 150 turns, what is the magnetic flux linkage in the coil? [2 marks]

(c) Over a period of 2.5 seconds the magnetic field is reduced uniformly to 1.5×10^{-3} T. What is the size of the e.m.f. induced across the ends of the coil? [3 marks]

Beware — physics can induce extreme confusion...

OK... I know that might have seemed a bit scary... but the more you go through it, the more it stops being a big scary monster of doom and just becomes another couple of equations you have to remember. Plus it's one of those things that makes you sound well clever... "What did you learn today Jim?", "Oh, just magnetic flux linkage Mum..."

Electromagnetic Induction

E.m.f. is a bit of a rebel... it always opposes the change that caused it.

The **Direction** of the **Induced E.m.f.** and **Current** are given by **Lenz's Law...**

LENZ'S LAW: The **induced e.m.f.** is always in such a **direction** as to **oppose** the **change** that caused it.

1) **Lenz's law** and **Faraday's law** can be **combined** to give one formula that works for both:

$$\text{Induced e.m.f. } (\varepsilon) = -\frac{d(N\phi)}{dt}$$

2) The **minus sign** shows the direction of the **induced e.m.f.**
3) The idea that an induced e.m.f. will **oppose** the change that caused it agrees with the principle of the **conservation of energy** — the **energy used** to pull a conductor through a magnetic field, against the **resistance** caused by magnetic **attraction**, is what **produces** the **induced current**.
4) **Lenz's law** can be used to find the **direction** of an **induced e.m.f.** and **current** in a conductor travelling at right angles to a magnetic field...

Jack thought the induction ceremony to get in the rugby club went a bit too far...

1) **Lenz's law** says that the **induced e.m.f.** will produce a force that **opposes** the motion of the conductor — in other words a **resistance**.
2) Using **Fleming's left-hand rule** (see p.17), point your thumb in the direction of the force of **resistance** — which is in the **opposite direction** to the motion of the conductor.
3) Your **second finger** will now give you the direction of the **induced e.m.f.**
4) If the conductor is **connected** as part of a **circuit**, a current will be induced in the **same direction** as the induced e.m.f.

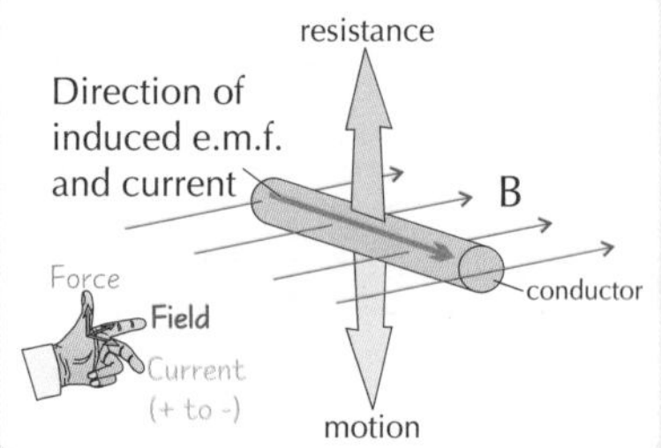

You Can **Change** the Amount of **E.m.f. Induced** in a Coil

You can change the voltage induced in the coil by changing one (or more) of the following factors:

1) The **angle between the coil and the field** — the more aligned the coil is to the field, the fewer field lines it will cut through, so the smaller the e.m.f. induced.
2) The **number of turns of the coil** — the higher the number of turns, the more points in the coil will cut each flux line, so the higher the e.m.f. induced in the coil.
3) The **area of the coil** — the larger the area of the coil, the more flux lines will pass though it and so the higher the e.m.f. induced.
4) The **magnetic field strength** (**flux density**) — the higher the flux density, the more flux lines there will be per unit area, so the coil will cut more flux, inducing a greater e.m.f.
5) The **angular speed** of the coil — increasing the rate the coil rotates at increases the number of flux lines cut by the coil in a given time, and so increases the voltage induced in the coil.

An **Alternator** is a **Generator** of **Alternating Current**

1) **Generators**, or dynamos, **convert** kinetic energy into **electrical energy** — they **induce** an electric **current** by **rotating** a **coil** in a magnetic field.
2) The diagram shows a simple **alternator** — a generator of **AC**.
It has **slip rings** and **brushes** to connect the coil to an external circuit.
3) The output **voltage** and **current** change direction with every **half rotation** of the coil, producing **alternating current** (**AC**).

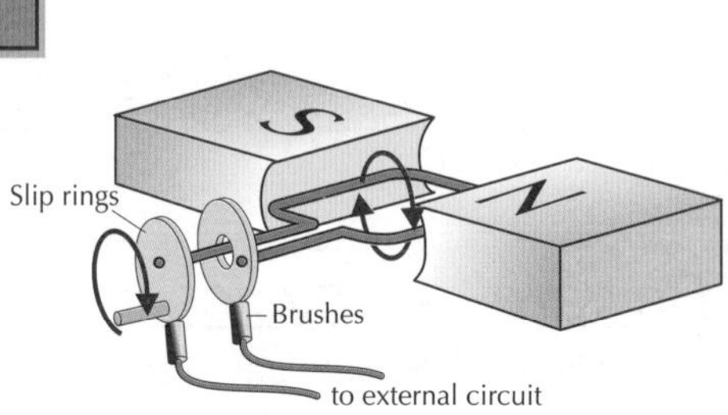

Electromagnetic Induction

Transformers are like voltage aerobics instructors. They say step up, the voltage goes up. They say step down, the voltage goes down. They say star jump, and the voltage does nothing because neither of them are alive — it's just induction.

Transformers *Work by Electromagnetic* ***Induction***

1) **Transformers** are devices that make use of electromagnetic induction to **change** the size of the **voltage** for an **alternating current**. They use the principle of flux linking using two coils of wire.

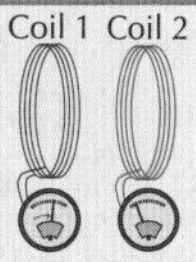

For example, if the **voltage** in **Coil 1** is **increased**, an **e.m.f.** and a **current** will be **induced** in **Coil 2**.

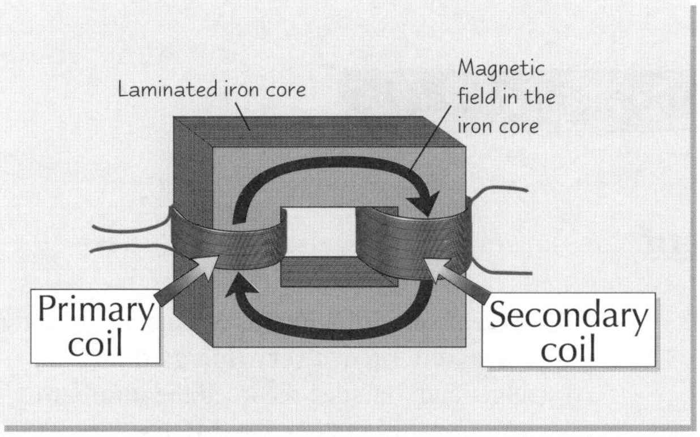

2) An alternating current flowing in the **primary** (or input) **coil** produces **magnetic flux**.

3) The **magnetic field** is passed through the **iron core** to the **secondary** (or output) coil, where it **induces** an alternating **voltage** of the same frequency.

4) **Step-up** transformers **increase** the **voltage** by having **more turns** on the **secondary** coil than the primary. **Step-down** transformers **reduce** the voltage by having **fewer** turns on the secondary coil.

Practice Questions

Q1 State Lenz's law.

Q2 Give two things you could do to increase the e.m.f. induced in a coil of wire moved through a uniform magnetic field.

Q3 State two uses of electromagnetic induction.

Exam Questions

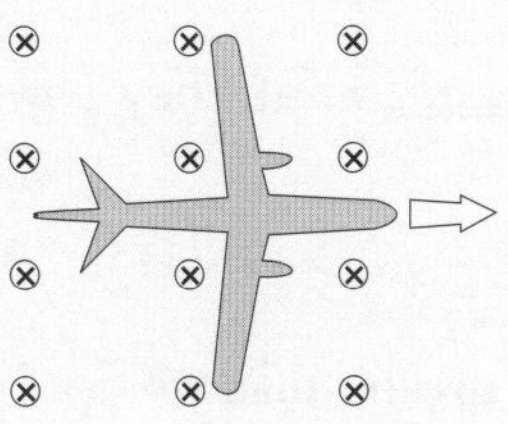

Q1 An aeroplane with a wingspan of 30 m flies at a speed of 100 ms^{-1} perpendicular to the Earth's magnetic field, as shown. The Earth's magnetic field at the aeroplane's location is 60×10^{-6} T.

(a) Calculate the induced e.m.f. between the wing-tips. [2 marks]

(b) Complete the diagram to show the direction of the induced e.m.f. between the wing-tips. [1 mark]

Q2 The graph below shows how the flux through a coil varies over time.

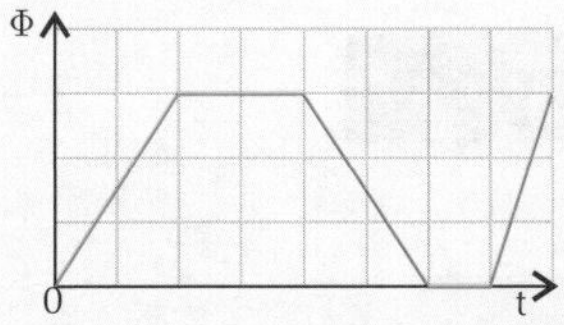

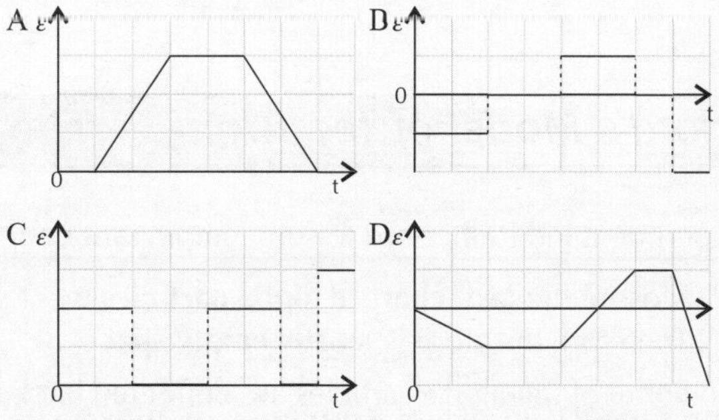

Which graph, **A** to **D**, shows how the induced e.m.f. in the coil varies over this same time period? [1 mark]

Lenz's law — the code of practice for opticians...

Make sure you know the difference between flux and flux linkage, and that you can calculate both. Then all you need to learn is that the induced e.m.f. is proportional to minus the rate of change of flux linkage — and that's it. Remember when you're using Fleming's left-hand rule to work out the direction of the induced e.m.f. that you need to point your thumb in the opposite direction to the direction the conductor is moving in...

The Nuclear Atom

You'll probably be pretty familiar with the nuclear model of the atom, but it wasn't so long ago that scientists had a very different idea of atomic structure. Since then, they've discovered tons of subatomic particles, as you'll learn on page 26.

The **Thomson Model** was Popular in the **19th Century**

Until the early 20th century, physicists believed that the atom was a **positively charged globule** with **negatively charged electrons sprinkled** in it. This "**plum pudding**" model of the atom was known as the **Thomson Model.** This all changed in 1909 when the **Rutherford scattering experiment** was done.

In Rutherford's laboratory, **Hans Geiger** and **Ernest Marsden** studied the scattering of **alpha particles** by **thin metal foils.**

Rutherford's Experiment **Disproved** the **Thomson Model**

Rutherford's Scattering Experiment

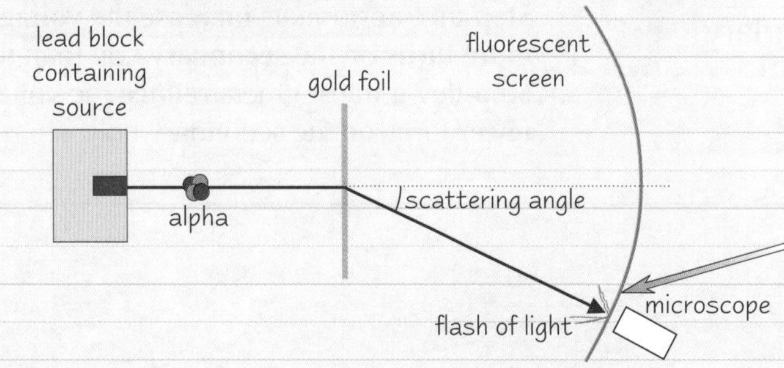

A **stream of alpha particles** from a radioactive source were fired at **very thin gold foil**. Geiger and Marsden recorded the **number** of alpha particles scattered at **different angles**.

When alpha particles from a radioactive source strike a fluorescent screen a tiny visible flash of light is produced.

If the **Thomson model** was right, all the flashes should have been seen within a **small angle** of the beam.

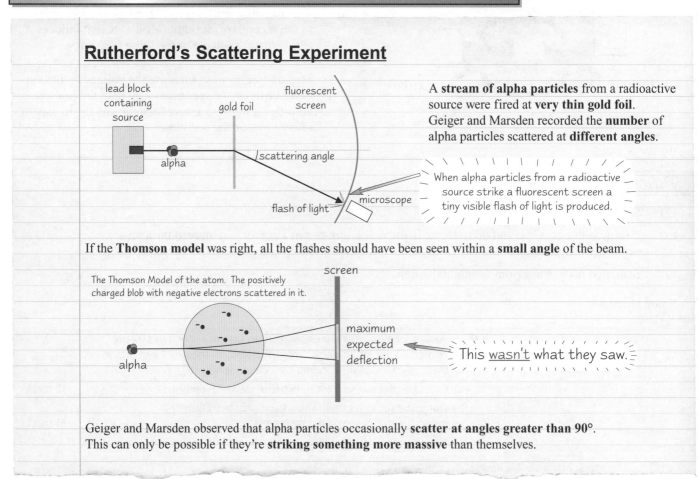

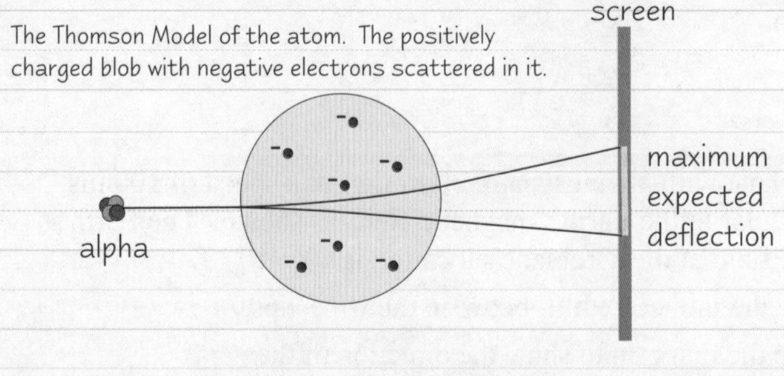

This wasn't what they saw.

Geiger and Marsden observed that alpha particles occasionally **scatter at angles greater than 90°**. This can only be possible if they're **striking something more massive** than themselves.

Rutherford's **Model** of the **Atom — The Nuclear Model**

This experiment led Rutherford to some **important conclusions:**

1) Most of the **fast**, **charged alpha particles** went **straight through** the gold foil. Therefore the atom is **mostly empty space**.
2) **Some** of the alpha particles are **deflected back** through **significant angles**, so the **centre** of the atom must be **tiny** but contain **a lot of mass**. Rutherford named this the **nucleus**.
3) The **alpha particles** were **repelled**, so the **nucleus** must have **positive charge**.
4) **Atoms** are **neutral overall** so the **electrons** must be on the outside of the atom — separating one atom from the next.

The Nuclear Atom

Atoms are made up of Protons, Neutrons and Electrons

Inside **every atom**, there's a **nucleus** containing **protons** and **neutrons**.
Protons and **neutrons** are both known as **nucleons**. **Orbiting** this core are the **electrons**.

This is the **nuclear model** of the atom.

The diagram shows **neutral oxygen**, with **eight protons** and **eight electrons**.

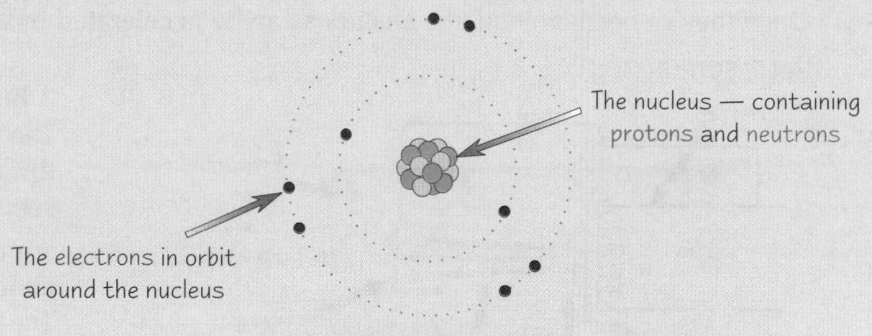

You have to know the **properties** of **electrons**, **protons** and **neutrons** for the exam — make sure you **learn this table**.

The masses in the table are given in **atomic mass units** (**u**).
1 u is equal to **one-twelfth** the mass of an atom of **carbon-12** — which means it's almost exactly the same as the **mass of a proton** or neutron.

$1\text{ u} = 1.66 \times 10^{-27}\text{ kg}$

Particle	Charge	Relative Mass
Proton	Positive, +1	1
Neutron	Neutral, 0	1
Electron	Negative, −1	0.0005

The Proton Number is the Number of Protons in the Nucleus

No... really.

The **proton number** is sometimes called the **atomic number**, and has the **symbol Z** (I'm sure it makes sense to someone). **Z** is just the **number of protons** in the nucleus.

It's the **proton number** that **defines** the **element** — **no two elements** will have the **same** number of protons.

In a **neutral atom**, the number of **electrons equals** the number of **protons**. The element's **reactions** and **chemical behaviour** depend on the number of **electrons**. So the **proton number** tells you a lot about its **chemical properties**.

The Nucleon Number is the Total Number of Protons and Neutrons

The **nucleon number** is also called the **mass number**, and has the **symbol A** (*shrug*).
It tells you how many **protons** and **neutrons** are in the nucleus. Each **proton or neutron** has a **mass** of (approximately) **1 atomic mass unit**. The mass of an electron compared with a nucleon is virtually nothing, so the **number** of **nucleons** is about the same as the **atom's mass** (in atomic mass units).

Practice Questions

Q1 Explain how alpha particle scattering shows that a nucleus is both small and positively charged.

Q2 List the particles that make up the atom and give their charges and relative masses.

Q3 Define the proton number and nucleon number.

Exam Question

Q1 A beam of alpha particles is directed onto a very thin gold film.

(a) Explain why the majority of alpha particles are not scattered. [2 marks]

(b) Explain how alpha particles are scattered by atomic nuclei. [3 marks]

Alpha scattering — it's positively repulsive...

The important things to learn from these two pages are the nuclear model for the structure of the atom (i.e. a large mass nucleus surrounded by orbiting electrons) and how Geiger and Marsden's alpha-particle scattering experiment gives evidence that supports this model. Once you know that, take a deep breath — it's about to get a little more confusing.

Particle Accelerators

Particle accelerators are devices that (surprisingly) accelerate particles, using electric and magnetic fields.

Electron Guns Produce Electrons by Thermionic Emission

1) When you **heat** a **metal**, its **free electrons** gain a load of **thermal energy**.
2) Give them **enough energy** and they **break free** from the surface of the metal — this is called **thermionic emission**.
3) Once they've been emitted, the electrons can be **accelerated** by an **electric field** in an **electron gun**:

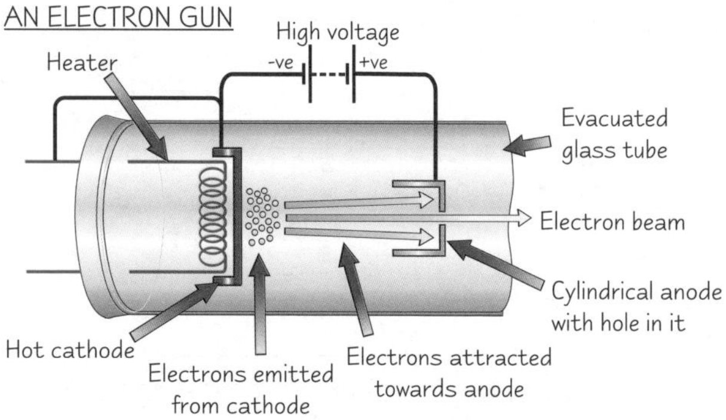

A **heating coil** heats the metal cathode.
The electrons that are emitted are **accelerated** towards the **cylindrical anode** by the electric field set up by the high voltage.

Some electrons pass through a **little hole** in the **anode**, making a narrow electron beam.
The electrons in the beam move at a **constant velocity** because there's **no field** beyond the anode — i.e., there's **no force**.

An Electron Microscope uses an Electron Gun

In an electron microscope, the **stream of electrons** from the **gun** is **focused** onto the sample using a magnetic field. Electron microscopes can **resolve very fine details** because electrons show **wave-like properties**. The **"electron wavelength"** is related to its **momentum** by the de Broglie equation:

$$\lambda = \frac{h}{p}$$

where **λ = wavelength**, **p = momentum** and **h** = Planck's constant = 6.63×10^{-34} Js.

To resolve detail around the size of an atom, the electron wavelength needs to be around 0.1 nm.

The Electronvolt is Defined Using Accelerated Charges

1) The **kinetic energy** that a particle with charge ***Q*** **gains** when it's **accelerated** through a p.d. of ***V*** volts is ***QV*** joules. That just comes from the definition of the **volt** (JC^{-1}).
2) If you replace ***Q*** in the equation with the charge of a **single electron**, **e**, you get: $\frac{1}{2}mv^2 = eV$
3) From this you can define a new **unit of energy** called the **electronvolt** (**eV**):

   1 electronvolt is the **kinetic energy carried** by an **electron** after it has been **accelerated** through a **potential difference** of **1 volt**.

4) So, the **energy in eV** of an electron accelerated by a potential difference is:

   energy gained by electron (eV) = accelerating voltage (V)

Conversion factor: 1 eV = 1.6×10^{-19} J

The unit MeV is the mega-electronvolt (equal to 1.6×10^{-13} J) and GeV is the giga-electronvolt (1.6×10^{-10} J).

Linear Particle Accelerators (Linacs) Cause High-Energy Collisions

1) A **linear particle accelerator** (**linac**) is a long **straight** tube containing a series of **electrodes**.
2) **High-frequency alternating current** is applied to the electrodes so that their **charge** continuously **changes** between + and –.
3) The alternating current is **timed** so that the particles are always **attracted** to the **next electrode** in the accelerator and **repelled** from the **previous** one.
4) A particle's **speed increases** each time it **passes** an electrode.
5) The **high-energy particles** leaving a linac **collide** with a **fixed target** at the end of the tube.

A linear particle accelerator

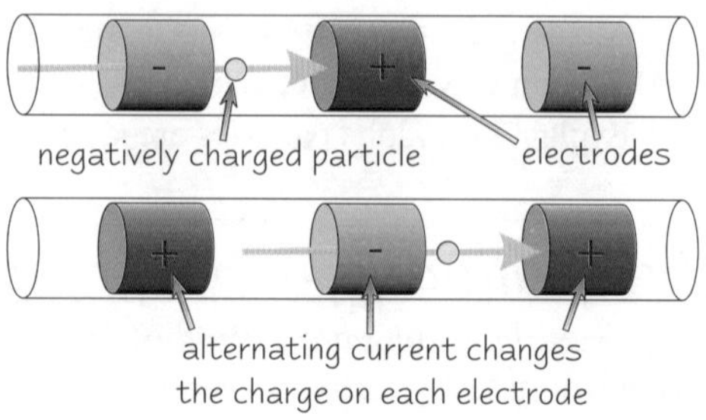

Particle Accelerators

A Cyclotron is a Circular Particle Accelerator

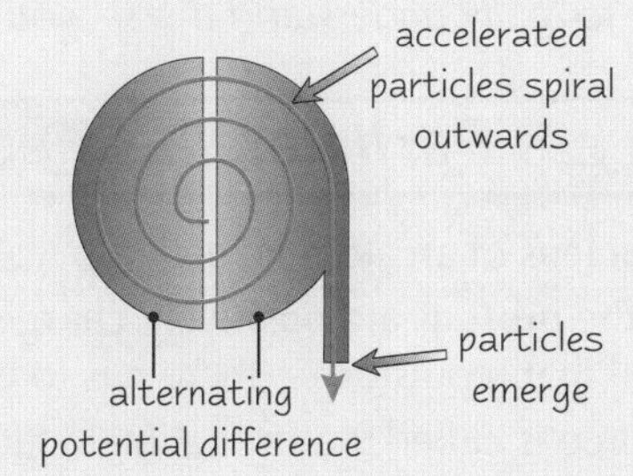

1) A cyclotron uses **two semicircular electrodes** to accelerate protons or other charged particles across a gap.
2) Since it is **circular**, a cyclotron can take up **much less room** than a linear accelerator.
3) An **alternating potential difference** is applied between the electrodes — as the **particles** are **attracted** from one side to the other their **energy increases** (i.e. they are **accelerated**).
4) A **magnetic field** is used to keep the particles moving in a **circular motion** (in the diagram on the right, the magnetic field would be perpendicular to the page).
5) The combination of the **electric** and **magnetic fields** makes the particles **spiral outwards** as their energy increases.

The Mass of Particles Increases with Speed

1) According to **special relativity**, as you **accelerate** an object you **increase** its **mass**.
2) The increase in mass **isn't usually noticeable** — it's only when you get close to the **speed of light** that it starts to have a **big effect**.
3) This means that as an object, like a **particle** in an **accelerator**, **travels faster and faster** its **mass gets greater and greater**. As the mass of the particle increases, it gets **harder** to accelerate it.
4) This effect **limits** how much you can accelerate a particle in a cyclotron. Protons can be accelerated to energies of around **20 MeV**. If you want higher energies than that, you have to use a different type of accelerator called a **synchrotron**.

Kim knew that slowing down wouldn't decrease her mass — but it was a good excuse.

Practice Questions

Q1 What is meant by thermionic emission?

Q2 Sketch a labelled diagram of an electron gun that could be used to accelerate electrons.

Q3 Explain how particles are accelerated in a linear accelerator.

Q4 What forces act on a particle in a cyclotron?

Exam Questions

(Use electron mass = 9.1×10^{-31} kg, electron charge = -1.6×10^{-19} C and h = 6.63×10^{-34} Js)

Q1 An electron is accelerated through a potential difference of 1 kV.

(a) Write down its energy in eV. [1 mark]

(b) Calculate its energy in joules. [1 mark]

(c) Calculate its speed in ms^{-1} and express this as a percentage of the speed of light (3.0×10^8 ms^{-1}). [3 marks]

Q2 A cyclotron is used to accelerate particles to very high speeds.
Outline the function of the electric and magnetic fields in a cyclotron. [2 marks]

Q3 The wavelength of the electrons in a microscope is 0.15 nm. The velocity of the electrons is approximately:
A 4.4×10^6 m s^{-1} **B** 4.9×10^6 m s^{-1} **C** 6.5×10^6 m s^{-1} **D** 1.0×10^7 m s^{-1}. [1 mark]

Smash high-energy particles together to see what they're made of...

A famous particle accelerator (in the physics world) is the Large Hadron Collider (LHC) found at CERN on the Swiss-French border — this accelerator is a whopping 27 km loop... Make sure you understand how the two types of particle accelerator on this page work — and don't forget to learn the equations on page 24 either.

Classification of Particles

There are loads of different types of particle apart from the ones you get in normal matter (protons, neutrons, etc.). They only appear in cosmic rays and in particle accelerators, and they often decay very quickly, so they're difficult to get a handle on. Nonetheless, you need to learn about a load of them and their properties.

Don't expect to really understand this — you only need to learn it. Stick with it — you'll get there.

Hadrons *are* ***Particles*** *that Feel the* ***Strong Interaction*** *(e.g. Protons and Neutrons)*

1) The **nucleus** of an atom is made up from **protons** and **neutrons** (déjà vu).
2) Since the **protons** are **positively charged** you might think that the nucleus would **fly apart** with all that repulsion — there has to be a strong **force** holding the **p**'s and **n**'s together.
3) That force is called the strong interaction (who said physicists lack imagination...)
4) Not all particles can feel the strong interaction — the ones that can are called hadrons.
5) Hadrons aren't **fundamental** particles. They're made up of **smaller particles** called **quarks** (see page 30).
6) There are **two** types of **hadron** — **baryons** and **mesons**.

Protons *and* ***Neutrons*** *are* ***Baryons***

1) It's helpful to think of **protons** and **neutrons** as **two versions** of the **same particle** — the **nucleon**. They just have **different electric charges**.
2) As well as **protons** and **neutrons**, there are **other baryons** that you don't get in normal matter — like **sigmas** (Σ) — they're **short-lived** and you **don't** need to **know about them** for A2 (woohoo!).

The ***Proton*** *is the* ***Only Stable Baryon***

All baryons except protons decay to a **proton**.
Most physicists think that protons don't **decay**.

Some theories predict that protons should decay with a very long half-life of about 10^{32} years — but there's no experimental evidence for it at the moment.

Baryon and Meson fel the strong interactio

The ***Number of Baryons*** *in a reaction is called the* ***Baryon Number***

Baryon number is the number of baryons. (A bit like **nucleon number** but including unusual baryons like Σ too.)
The **proton** and the **neutron** each have a baryon number **B = +1**.
The **total baryon number** in **any** particle reaction **never changes**.

The ***Mesons*** *You Need to Know About are* ***Pions and Kaons***

1) **All mesons** are **unstable** and have **baryon number B = 0** (because they're not baryons).
2) **Pions** (π-mesons) are the **lightest mesons**. You get **three versions** with different **electric charges** — π^+, π^0 and π^-. Pions were **discovered** in **cosmic rays**. You get **loads** of them in **high-energy particle collisions** like those studied at the **CERN** particle accelerator.
3) **Kaons** (**K**-mesons) are **heavier** and more **unstable** than **pions**. You get different ones like K^+, K^- and K^0.
4) Mesons **interact** with **baryons** via the **strong interaction**.

Pion interactions swap p's with n's and n's with p's, but leave the overall baryon number unchanged.

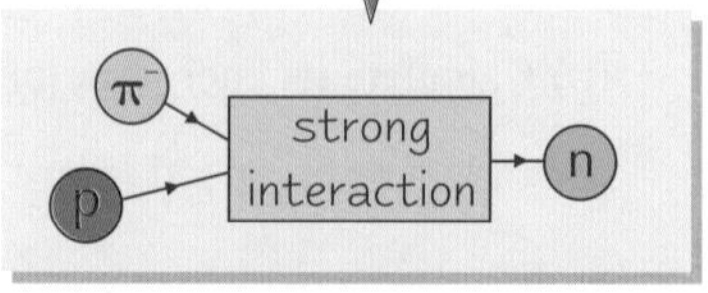

Summary *of* ***Hadron Properties***

DON'T PANIC if you don't understand all this yet. For now, just **learn** these properties. You'll need to work through to the end of page 32 to see how it **all fits in**.

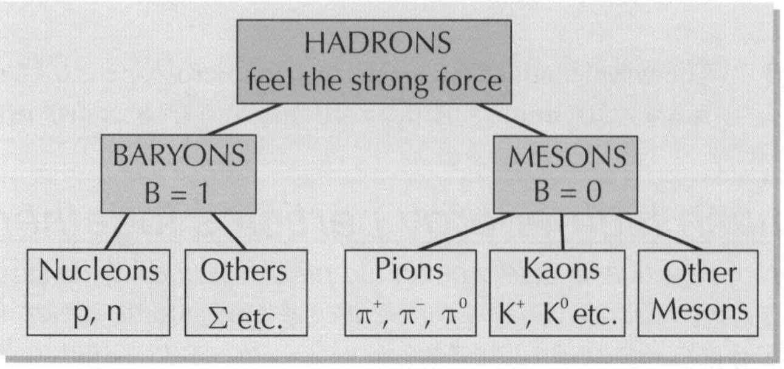

Classification of Particles

Leptons Don't feel the Strong Interaction *(e.g. Electrons and Neutrinos)*

1) **Leptons** are **fundamental particles** and they **don't** feel the **strong interaction**. The only way they can **interact** with other particles is via the **weak interaction** and gravity (and the electromagnetic force as well if they're charged).
2) **Electrons** (e^-) are **stable** and very **familiar** but — you guessed it — there are also **two more leptons** called the **muon** (μ^-) and the **tau** (τ^-) that are just like **heavy electrons**.
3) **Muons** and **taus** are **unstable**, and **decay** eventually into **ordinary electrons**.
4) The **electron**, **muon** and **tau** each come with their **own neutrino**: ν_e, ν_μ and ν_τ.
5) **Neutrinos** have **zero** or **almost zero mass** and **zero electric charge** — so they don't do much. In fact, a neutrino can **pass right through the Earth** without **anything** happening to it.

ν is the Greek letter "nu".

You Have to Count the Three Types of Lepton Separately

Like the baryon number, the lepton number is just the number of leptons.

Each lepton is given a **lepton number** of **+1**, but the **electron**, **muon** and **tau** types of lepton have to be **counted separately**.

You get **three different** lepton numbers: L_e, L_μ and L_τ.

Name	Symbol	Charge	L_e	L_μ	L_τ
electron	e^-	–1	+1	0	0
electron neutrino	ν_e	0	+1	0	0
muon	μ^-	–1	0	+1	0
muon neutrino	ν_μ	0	0	+1	0
tau	τ^-	–1	0	0	+1
tau neutrino	ν_τ	0	0	0	+1

Neutrons Decay into Protons

The **neutron** is an **unstable particle** that **decays** into a **proton**. (But it's much more stable when it's part of a nucleus.) It's really just an **example** of β^- decay:

$$n \rightarrow p + e^- + \bar{\nu}_e$$

The antineutrino has $L_e = -1$ so the total lepton number is zero. Antineutrino? Yes, well I haven't mentioned antiparticles yet. Just wait for the next page ...

Free neutrons (i.e. ones not held in a nucleus) have a half-life of about 15 minutes.

Practice Questions

Q1 List the differences between a hadron and a lepton.

Q2 Which is the only stable baryon?

Q3 A particle collision at CERN produces 2 protons, 3 pions and 1 neutron. What is the total baryon number of these particles?

Q4 Which two particles have lepton number $L_\tau = +1$?

Exam Questions

Q1 List all the decay products of the neutron. Explain why this decay cannot be due to the strong interaction. [3 marks]

Q2 Initially the muon was incorrectly identified as a meson. Explain why the muon is not a meson. [3 marks]

Go back to the top of page 26 — do not pass GO, do not collect £200...

Do it. Go back and read it again. I promise — read these pages about 3 or 4 times and you'll start to see a pattern. There are hadrons that feel the force, leptons that don't. Hadrons are either baryons or mesons, and they're all weird except for those well-known baryons: protons and neutrons. There are loads of leptons, including good old electrons.

Antiparticles

More stuff that seems to laugh in the face of common sense — but actually, antiparticles help to explain a lot in particle physics... (Oh, and if you haven't read pages 26 and 27 yet then go back and read them now — no excuses, off you go...)

Antiparticles were Predicted Before they were Discovered

When **Paul Dirac** wrote down an equation obeyed by **electrons**, he found a kind of **mirror image** solution.

1) It predicted the existence of a particle like the **electron** but with **opposite electric charge** — the **positron**.
2) The **positron** turned up later in a cosmic ray experiment. Positrons are **antileptons** so **L_e = –1** for them. They have **identical mass** to electrons but they carry a **positive** charge.

Nice one Paul. Now we've got twice as many things to worry about.

Every Particle has an Antiparticle

Each particle type has a **corresponding antiparticle** with the **same mass** but with **opposite charge**. For instance, an **antiproton** is a **negatively charged** particle with the same mass as the **proton**.

Even the shadowy **neutrino** has an antiparticle version called the **antineutrino** — it doesn't do much either.

Particle	Symbol	Charge	B	L_e	Antiparticle	Symbol	Charge	B	L_e
proton	p	+1	+1	0	antiproton	$\bar{p}$	–1	–1	0
neutron	n	0	+1	0	antineutron	$\bar{n}$	0	–1	0
electron	e	–1	0	+1	positron	e^+	+1	0	–1
electron neutrino	ν_e	0	0	+1	electron antineutrino	$\bar{\nu}_e$	0	0	–1

You can Create Matter and Antimatter from Energy

You've probably heard about the **equivalence** of energy and mass. It all comes out of Einstein's special theory of relativity. **Energy** can turn into **mass** and **mass** can turn into **energy** if you know how — all you need is one fantastic and rather famous formula. →

$$E = mc^2$$

If you've done any chemistry, you'll know that when you carry out a reaction the **mass of your reactants** will always equal the **mass of your products** — i.e. **mass is conserved**. In **nuclear reactions**, the **mass** of the particles you start with might be **more** or **less** than the mass of the particles you end up with. This happens when **energy** is **converted** to mass or mass to energy. This time it's the **total mass and energy** that's **conserved**.

When **energy** is converted into **mass** you have to make **equal amounts** of **matter** and **antimatter**.

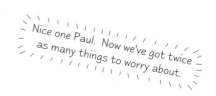

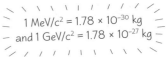

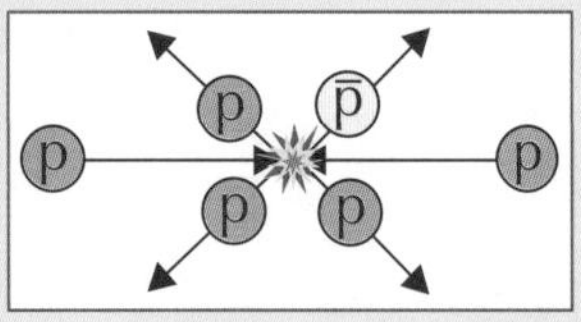

Fire **two protons** at each other at high speed and you'll end up with a lot of **energy** at the point of impact. This energy can form **more particles**.

If an extra **proton** is created, there has to be an **antiproton** made to go with it. It's called **pair production**.

When you're describing nuclear reactions, the SI units of **kilograms** and **joules** are **too big** to be easily used. Instead, the mega-electron volt, **MeV** (page 24), is used for **energy** and **atomic mass units**, **u** (page 23), or **eV/c²** are used for **mass**.

Conversion factor:

$$\frac{1\,\text{eV}}{c^2} = \frac{1.6\times10^{-19}\ \text{J}}{(3.0\times10^{8}\ \text{ms}^{-1})^2} = 1.78\times10^{-36}\ \text{kg}$$

$1\ \text{MeV}/c^2 = 1.78 \times 10^{-30}$ kg and $1\ \text{GeV}/c^2 = 1.78 \times 10^{-27}$ kg

Antiparticles

Each **Particle-Antiparticle Pair** is Produced from a **Single Photon**

Pair production only happens if **one gamma ray photon** has enough energy to produce that much mass. It also tends to happen near a **nucleus**, which helps conserve momentum.

You usually get **electron-positron** pairs produced (rather than any other pair) — because they have a relatively **low mass**.

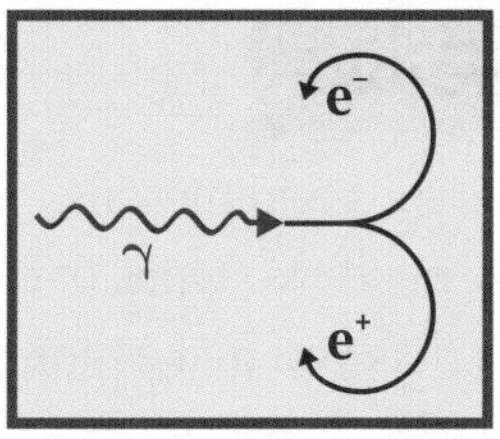

The particle tracks are curved because there's usually a magnetic field present in particle physics experiments (see p. 33). They curve in opposite directions because of the opposite charges on the electron and positron.

Example An electron and a positron are produced from a single photon. Find the minimum energy of the photon. (The rest mass of an electron, $m_e = 9.11\times10^{-31}$ kg.)

The minimum energy the photon must have is enough energy to produce the particles' mass alone (the particles will have no kinetic energy).
Energy before = Energy after.
So the energy of the photon $\geq 2m_ec^2 = 2 \times 9.11\times10^{-31} \times (3\times10^8)^2 = 1.64 \times10^{-13}$ J = **1.0 MeV**

The **Opposite** of **Pair Production** is **Annihilation**

When a **particle** meets its **antiparticle** the result is **annihilation**. All the **mass** of the particle and antiparticle gets converted to **energy**. In ordinary matter antiparticles can only exist for a fraction of a second before this happens, so you won't see many of them.

The electron and positron annihilate and their mass is converted into the energy of a pair of gamma ray photons.

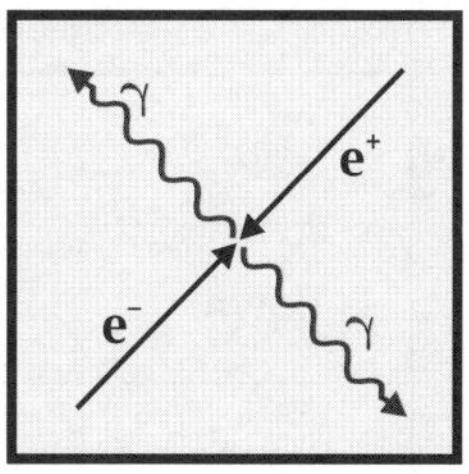

Mesons are Their **Own Antiparticles**

Just before you leave this bit it's worth mentioning that the π^- meson is just the **antiparticle** of the π^+ meson, and the **antiparticle** of a π^0 meson is **itself**. You'll see why on p. 31. So we don't need any more particles here... Phew.

(If you don't know what a meson is, look back at page 26.)

Practice Questions

Q1 Which antiparticle has zero charge and a baryon number of –1?

Q2 Describe the properties of an electron antineutrino.

Q3 What is pair production? What happens when a proton collides with an antiproton?

Exam Questions

Q1 Write down an equation for the reaction between a positron and an electron and give the name for this type of reaction. [2 marks]

Q2 According to Einstein, mass and energy are equivalent. Explain why the mass of a block of iron cannot be converted directly into energy. [2 marks]

Q3 Give a reason why the reaction $\mathbf{p + p \rightarrow p + p + n}$ is not possible. [1 mark]

Q4 An electron and a positron each have a kinetic energy of 300 MeV and a rest mass of 9.11×10^{-31} kg. They annihilate to produce two photons. Find the energy of one of the photons produced. [3 marks]

Now stop meson around and do some work...

The idea of every particle having an antiparticle might seem a bit strange, but just make sure you know the main points — a) if energy is converted into a particle, you also get an antiparticle, b) an antiparticle won't last long before it bumps into a particle and annihilates it with a big ba-da-boom, c) this releases the energy it took to make them to start with...

Quarks

*If you haven't read pages 26 to 29, do it now! For the rest of you — here are the **juicy bits** you've been waiting for. Particle physics makes **a lot more sense** when you look at quarks. More sense than it did before anyway.*

Quarks are Fundamental Particles

If that first sentence doesn't make much sense to you, read pages 26-29 — you have been warned... twice.

Quarks are the **building blocks** for **hadrons** (baryons and mesons).

1) To make **protons** and **neutrons** you only need two types of quark — the **up** quark (**u**) and the **down** quark (**d**).
2) An extra one called the **strange** quark (**s**) lets you make more particles with a property called **strangeness**.

Antiparticles of hadrons are made from **antiquarks**.

Quarks and Antiquarks have Opposite Properties

The **antiquarks** have **opposite properties** to the quarks — as you'd expect.

QUARKS

Name	Symbol	Charge	Baryon number	Strangeness
up	u	$+\,^2/_3$	$+\,^1/_3$	0
down	d	$-\,^1/_3$	$+\,^1/_3$	0
strange	s	$-\,^1/_3$	$+\,^1/_3$	–1

ANTIQUARKS

Name	Symbol	Charge	Baryon number	Strangeness
anti-up	$\bar{u}$	$-\,^2/_3$	$-\,^1/_3$	0
anti-down	$\bar{d}$	$+\,^1/_3$	$-\,^1/_3$	0
anti-strange	$\bar{s}$	$+\,^1/_3$	$-\,^1/_3$	+1

There are Three Other Types of Quark

Physicists began to accept the **quark model** when **scattering experiments** showed that **protons** were made up of **smaller particles**. But, the **symmetry** of the model also **predicted** three quarks that hadn't been detected. These quarks are **top** (**t**), **bottom** (**b**) and **charm** (**c**) — some of their properties are shown in the table.

Name	Symbol	Charge	Baryon number	Strangeness
top	t	$+\,^2/_3$	$+\,^1/_3$	0
bottom	b	$-\,^1/_3$	$+\,^1/_3$	0
charm	c	$+\,^2/_3$	$+\,^1/_3$	0

These three quarks have **all** since been **detected** in experiments using **particle accelerators**. They're all quite **unstable** though, so they don't occur in normal particles.

Quarks

Baryons are Made from Three Quarks

Evidence for quarks came from **hitting protons** with **high-energy electrons**.
The way the **electrons scattered** showed that there were **three concentrations of charge** (quarks) **inside** the proton.

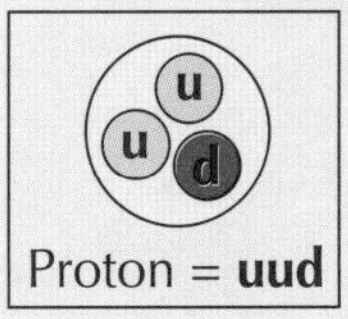

Total charge = 2/3 + 2/3 – 1/3 = 1
Baryon number = 1/3 + 1/3 + 1/3 = 1

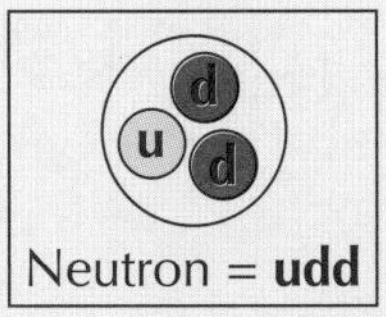

Total charge = 2/3 – 1/3 – 1/3 = 0
Baryon number = 1/3 + 1/3 + 1/3 = 1

Antiprotons are $\bar{u}\bar{u}\bar{d}$ and antineutrons are $\bar{u}\bar{d}\bar{d}$ — so no surprises there then.

Mesons are a Quark and an Antiquark

Pions are just made from combinations of **up**, **down**, **anti-up** and **anti-down** quarks.
Kaons have **strangeness** so you need to put in **s** quarks as well (remember, the **s** quark has a strangeness of S = –1).

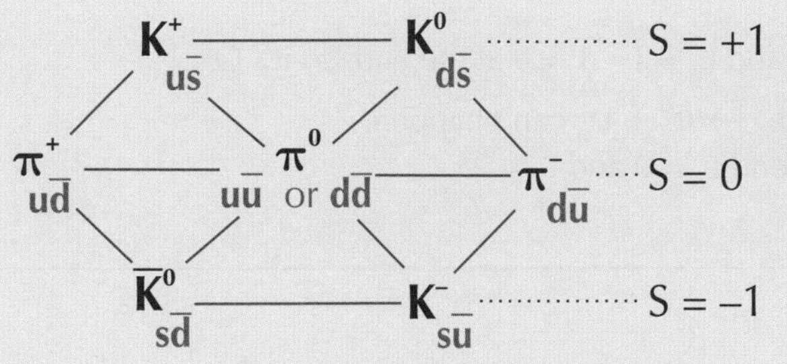

Physicists love patterns. Gaps in patterns like this predicted the existence of particles that were actually found later in experiments. Great stuff.

There's No Such Thing as a Free Quark

What if you **blasted** a **proton** with **enough energy** — could you **separate out** the quarks?
Nope. The energy just gets changed into more **quarks and antiquarks** — it's **pair production** again and you just make **mesons**.
It's not possible to get a quark by itself — this is called **quark confinement**.

Quark confinement: a dance interpretation.

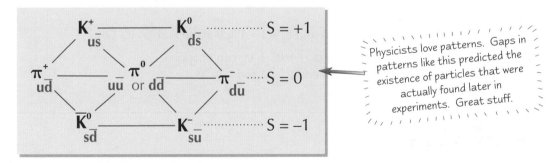

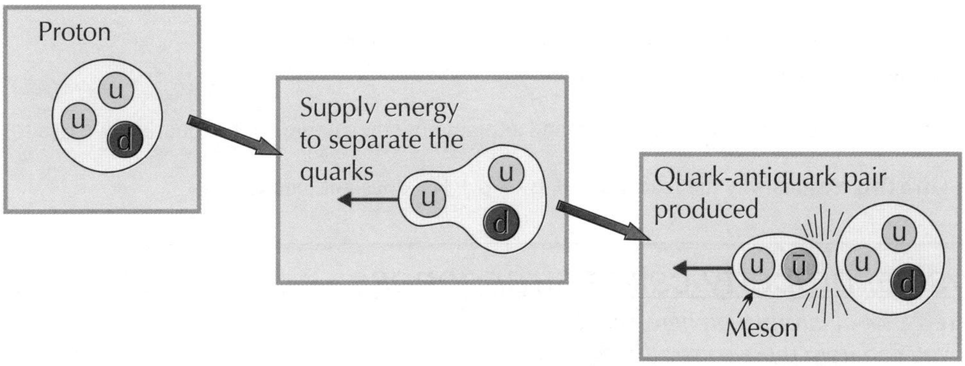

Quarks

More conservation? This is starting to sound like biology...

Five Properties are Conserved in Particle Reactions

Charge, Baryon Number, Energy and Momentum are Always Conserved

In **any** particle reaction, the **total charge** after the reaction must equal the total charge before the reaction.

The same goes for **baryon number**, e.g. the reaction $\mathbf{p} + \pi_0 \rightarrow \mathbf{p} + \mathbf{n}$ is fine for **charge**, but couldn't happen because the baryon number **increases** from 1 to 2.

Energy conservation is a bit complicated in particle reactions. Since mass and energy are equivalent (see p. 28), it's really **mass-energy** that's conserved — i.e. the total energy of the reaction if you convert the masses of all the particles into energy.

As with any other interaction, **momentum** has to be conserved.

If you look at particle tracks for the decay of a neutron into a proton from p. 27, it looks like momentum isn't quite conserved. That's because some momentum is carried by the antineutrino, which you can't see (see next page).

Conservation of Lepton Number is a Bit More Complicated

The **three types** of lepton number have to be conserved **separately**.

1) For example, the reaction
$\pi^- \rightarrow \mu^- + \bar{\nu}_\mu$ has $L_\mu = 0$ at the start and $L_\mu = 1 - 1 = 0$ at the end, so it's OK.

2) On the other hand, the reaction $\nu_\mu + \mu^- \rightarrow e^- + \nu_e$ can't happen.
At the start $L_\mu = 2$ and $L_e = 0$ but at the end $L_\mu = 0$ and $L_e = 2$.

Practice Questions

Q1 What is a quark?

Q2 Describe how a neutron is made up from quarks.

Q3 Which type of particle is made from a quark and an antiquark?

Q4 Explain why quarks are never observed on their own.

Q5 List five quantities that are conserved in particle reactions.

Exam Questions

Q1 A proton is composed of which combination of three quarks?
A ddd **B** uuu **C** ddu **D** uud [1 mark]

Q2 Give the quark composition of the π^- and explain how the charges of the quarks give rise to its charge. [2 marks]

Q3 Give two reasons why the reaction $\mathbf{p} + \mathbf{n} \rightarrow \mathbf{p} + \mathbf{K}^+$ does not happen. [2 marks]

A physical property called strangeness — how cool is that...

True, there's a lot of information here, but this page really does tie up a lot of the stuff on the last few pages. Learn as much as you can from these pages, then go back to page 26, and work back through to here. Don't expect to understand it all — but you will definitely find it much easier to learn when you can see how all the bits fit in together.

Detecting Particles

Luckily for us, charged particles affect atoms as they pass by — which means we can see what's going on...

Charged Particles Leave Tracks

When a charged particle passes through a substance it causes **ionisation** — electrons are knocked out of atoms. The particle leaves a **trail of ions** as it goes.

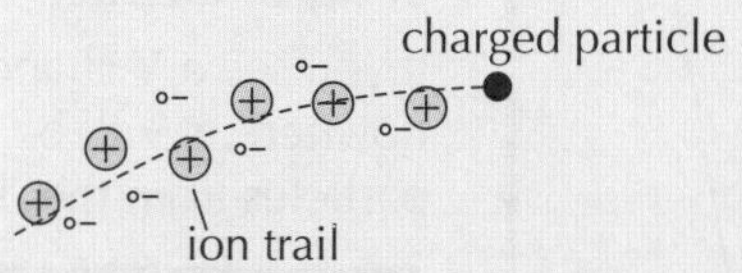

The easiest way to **detect** the particle is if you somehow make the **trail of ions show up** and then take a **photo**.

Ion tracks Cindy, not iron tracks...

Cloud Chambers and Bubble Chambers detect Charged Particles

1) **Cloud chambers** work using a **supercooled vapour** — that's something that's still a gas below its usual condensation temperature. The ions left by particles make the vapour **condense** and you get "**vapour trails**" (a bit like the ones left by jet planes).
Heavy, **short** tracks mean lots of ionisation, so those will be the **α-particles**. Fainter, **long** tracks are **β-particles**.

A cloud chamber photograph from an alpha source might look like this:

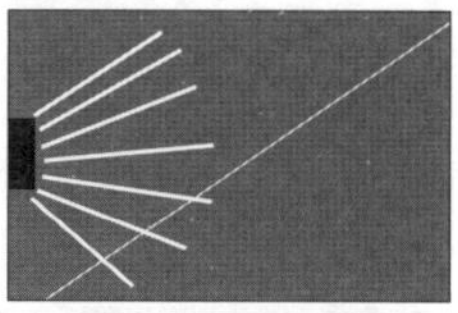

The thin line is a cosmic ray particle.

2) **Bubble chambers** are a bit like cloud chambers in reverse. Hydrogen is kept as a **liquid** above its normal **boiling point** by putting it under **pressure**. If the pressure is suddenly **reduced**, **bubbles of gas** will start to form in the places where there is a trail of ions. You have to take the photo **quickly** before the bubbles grow too big.
3) Both chambers only show up **charged particles**.

Charged Particles are Affected by a Magnetic Field

1) A **charged particle** in a **magnetic field** will experience a **force** — making the particle follow a **curved track**. (See Unit 4: Section 2.)

The radius of a charged particle's curved track, ***r***, is given by the equation:

$$r = \frac{p}{BQ}$$

The **larger** the curve **radius**, the **greater** the particle's **momentum**.

where p is the particle's momentum, B is the strength of the magnetic field and Q is the charge on the particle.

2) Positive and negative particles curve **opposite** ways — you can find out which is which using **Fleming's** left-hand rule (see p17).
3) You don't see neat circular patterns, but instead see **spirals**, as interactions with the detector decrease the energy (and so the momentum) of the particle.
4) You can also use this equation to find the magnetic field you need to keep a charge in a particular radius of circular path — very handy when you're dealing with **particle accelerators** (see p25).

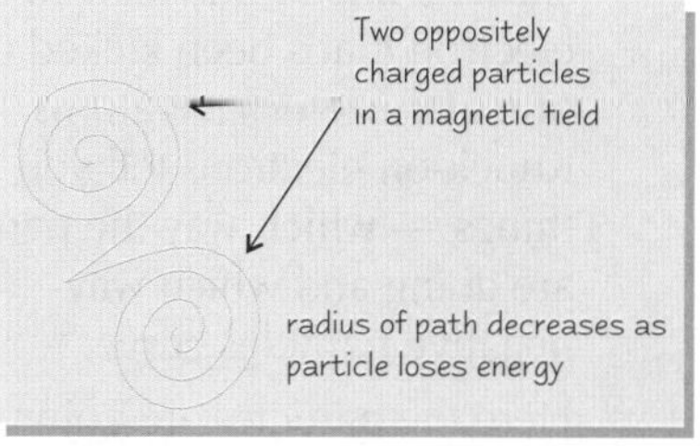

Charge, Energy and Momentum are Always Conserved

1) When you're looking at particle interactions and trying to work out what the blazes is going on, remember that **charge**, **momentum** and **energy** are always conserved.
2) If they're not conserved for the reaction you think you're looking at, you know you've got it wrong — it can't have happened.

Detecting Particles

And now for the best bit — the pretty pictures...

Neutral Particles Only Show Up When They Decay

Remember that **neutral** particles **don't** make tracks. You can only see them when they **decay** or **interact**.

If you see a **V** shape starting in the middle of nowhere, it will be two oppositely charged particles from the decay of a neutral particle.

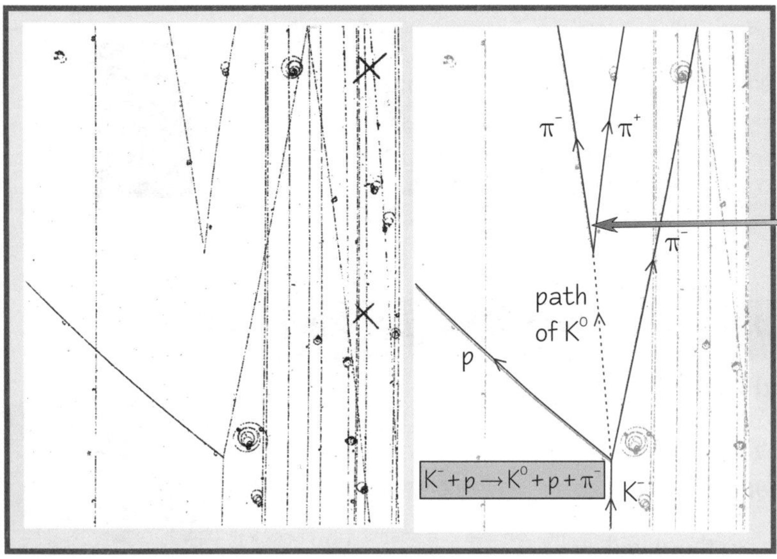

This V comes from the decay $K^0 \rightarrow \pi^+ + \pi^-$

Here the particles have so much momentum that the tracks are almost straight.

The **distance** from the **interaction point** to the V depends on the **half-life** of the neutral particle. Longer-lived particles travel **further** on average before they decay — but you have to be careful.

The particles are travelling **close to the speed of light** so they experience **relativistic time dilation**. That means that time seems to run **more slowly** for the moving particle than it does for you as a stationary observer — so they seem to **survive** for **much longer** than normal.

Real Bubble Chamber Photographs can be a bit Intimidating

At first sight the photo might look a bit of a mess with tracks everywhere.
Don't panic — start by finding the incoming beam...

1) The **straight** lines are from the incoming beam. Several particles will go straight through without doing anything — you can just ignore them.
2) Look for a little spiral coming from one of the straight tracks. It shows a **knock-on electron** — an electron that's been kicked out of one of the hydrogen atoms. Knock-on electrons tell you **two** things — **which way** the particles are going and which way negative particles **curve**.
3) Here the particles are going **up** and **negative** ones curl **clockwise**.
4) Find a **point** with **several** curved tracks coming from it — that's a reaction. You can identify positively and negatively charged particles from the **way they curve**.

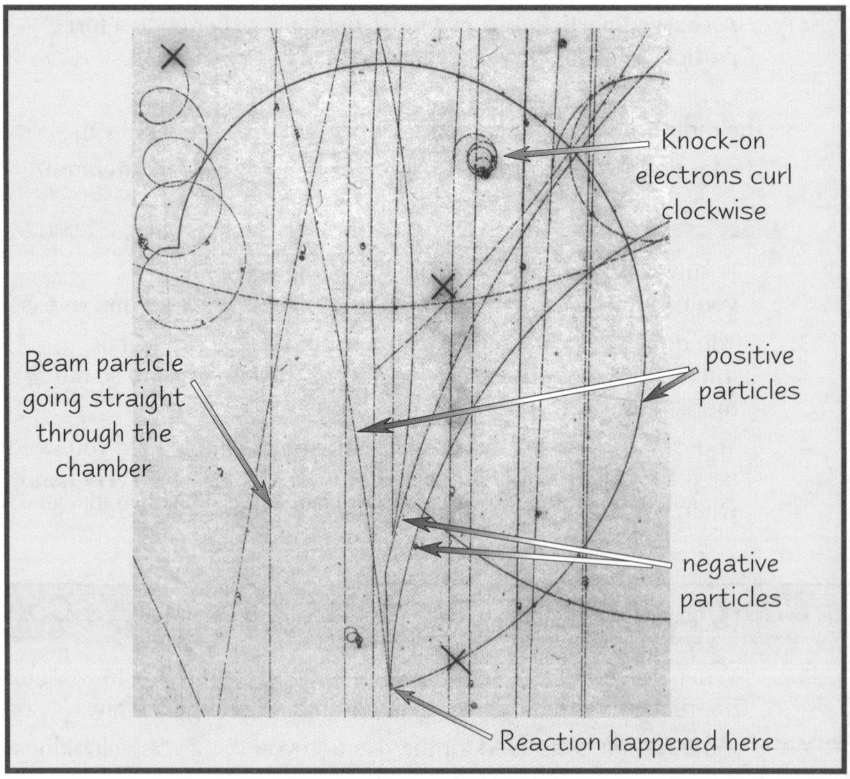

Detecting Particles

You can Calculate the Particle's **Momentum**

From the **radius** of the track, you can find the **momentum** of a particle.

Example

Particle X is an unstable neutral particle that quickly decays into a positron and an electron while in a bubble chamber. Both the electron and positron follow circular tracks in a 1.2×10^{-4} T magnetic field with an initial radius of 260 m.

Find the initial momentum of the electron ($e = 1.6 \times 10^{-19}$ C).

Using $r = \frac{p}{BQ}$, so $p = rBQ = 260 \times 1.2 \times 10^{-4} \times 1.6 \times 10^{-19}$ = **5.0×10^{-21} kg ms^{-1}**

Cloud Chambers and **Bubble Chambers aren't used** Any More

Nowadays, particle physicists use detectors that give out **electrical signals** that are sent **straight** to a **computer**. It's a bit easier than having a whole team of scientists squinting over thousands of photos. Modern detectors include **drift chambers**, **scintillation counters** and **solid state detectors**. You don't need to know any details about these for the exam.

Practice Questions

Q1 Describe how a cloud chamber works.

Q2 Explain the operation of a bubble chamber.

Q3 Which particles don't show up in bubble chamber photos?

Q4 How does the track of an electron show that the electron is losing energy?

Q5 Explain why a positron and an electron will move in opposite directions in a magnetic field.

Q6 Write down the equation used to relate the radius of a circular path taken by a charged particle in a magnetic field to the particle's momentum.

Exam Questions

Q1 Explain how the charges of particles can be found from their tracks in bubble chamber photographs. [3 marks]

Q2 Suggest one reason why antineutrinos are harder to detect than beta particles. [1 mark]

Q3 The reaction $\mathbf{p} + \mathbf{p} \rightarrow \mathbf{p} + \mathbf{n} + \pi^+ + \pi^0$ occurs in a bubble chamber.
Which products of this reaction will form tracks?

A π^0 and n **B** n and π^+ **C** π^+ and p **D** All of them [1 mark]

Q4 A photon, travelling through a bubble chamber, is converted into an $\mathbf{e^-}$ $\mathbf{e^+}$ pair.
Draw a sketch showing the tracks that would be formed by this reaction. [3 marks]

Q5 Particle Y decays to form an electron and a positron in a cloud chamber. The electron leaves a track with an initial radius of 3.2 m in a magnetic field of 1.8×10^{-6} T. Find the momentum of the electron. [2 marks]

Look, there's one...

*Typical. They now have an easy way of detecting particles — but you have to learn the methods that are a) harder, and b) now completely obsolete. *sigh* I suppose it's quite nice to actually see the pictures though.*

Heat and Temperature

You need energy to heat something up, and very cold things have very little energy. Everything comes down to energy.

Specific Heat Capacity is how much Energy it Takes to Heat Something

When you heat something, its particles get more **kinetic energy** and its **temperature** rises.

The **specific heat capacity** (*c*) of a substance is the amount of **energy** needed to **raise** the **temperature** of **1 kg** of the substance by **1 K** (or 1°C).

or put another way: **energy change = mass × specific heat capacity × change in temperature**

in symbols: $\Delta E = mc\Delta\theta$ ← ΔQ is sometimes used instead of ΔE for the change in thermal energy.

ΔE is the energy change in J, m is the mass in kg and $\Delta\theta$ is the temperature change in K or °C. Units of **c** are $\text{J kg}^{-1}\,\text{K}^{-1}$ or $\text{J kg}^{-1}\,°\text{C}^{-1}$.

You can Measure Specific Heat Capacity in the Laboratory

The **method**'s the same for **solids** and **liquids**, but the **set-up**'s a little bit different:

Specific Heat Capacity of a Solid

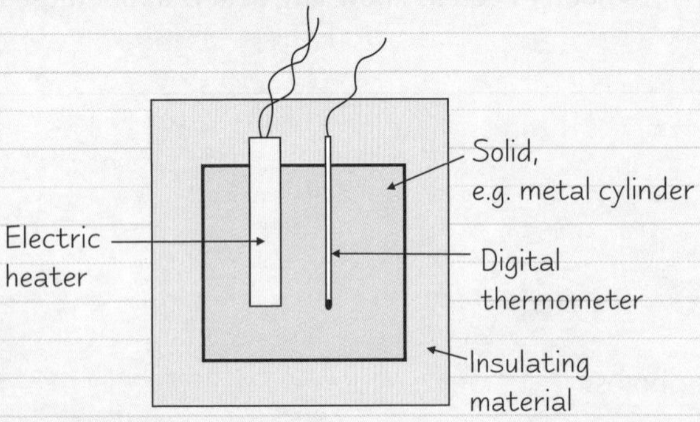

Specific Heat Capacity of a Liquid

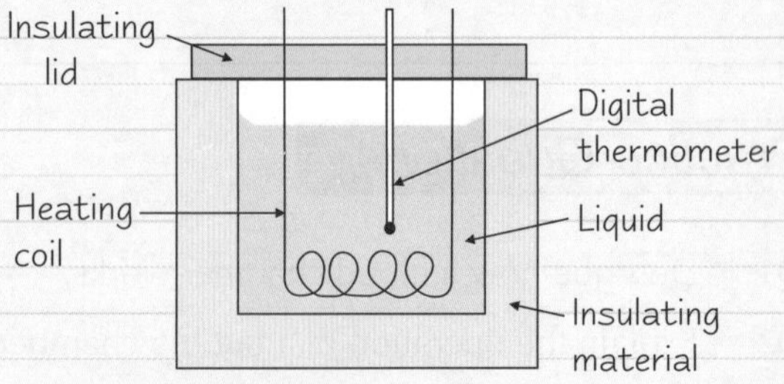

Method for Both

1) **Heat** the substance with the heater. You need a **temperature rise** of about 10 K to get an **accurate** value of **c**. [NB The insulation **reduces** the heat loss, but it's far from perfect. If you're really keen, start **below** and finish **above** room temperature to **cancel out** gains and losses.]

2) With an ammeter and voltmeter attached to your **electric heater** you can work out the energy supplied. Here's the circuit:

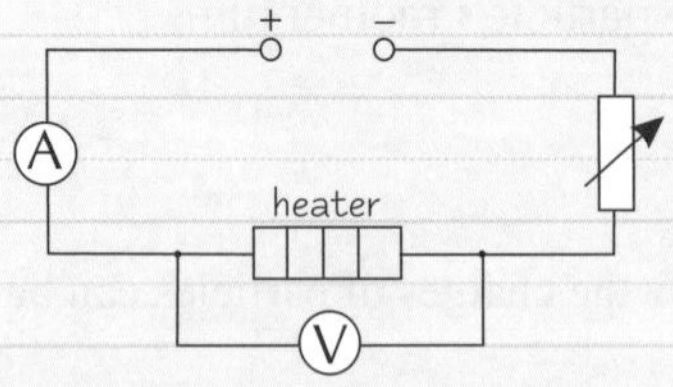

Calculate the energy (ΔE) using: $\Delta E = VI\Delta t$

where V is the heater voltage, I is the current and Δt is the time in seconds (you should know this from AS).

3) Plug your data into: $\Delta E = mc\Delta\theta$ to calculate **c**.

The value you end up with for c will probably be too high by quite a long way. That's because some of the energy from the heater gets transferred to the air and the container.

Example You heat 0.25 kg of water from 12.1 °C to 22.9 °C with an electric immersion heater. The heater has a voltage of 11.2 V and a current of 5.3 A, and is switched on for 205 s.

Electrical energy supplied = $VI\Delta t$ = 11.2 × 5.3 × 205 = 12 170 J

Temperature rise = 22.9 – 12.1 = 10.8 °C = 10.8 K

So $c = \dfrac{12170}{0.25 \times 10.8} = 4510\ \text{J kg}^{-1}\text{K}^{-1}$ ← The actual value for water is $4180\ \text{J kg}^{-1}\,\text{K}^{-1}$. This result's too big, because ΔE is bigger than it should be (like I said before).

Heat and Temperature

There's an Absolute Scale of Temperature

There is a **lowest possible temperature** called **absolute zero***. Absolute zero is given a value of **zero kelvin**, written **0 K**, on the absolute temperature scale.

At **0 K** all particles have the **minimum** possible **kinetic energy** — everything pretty much stops — at higher temperatures, particles have more energy. In fact, with the **Kelvin scale**, a particle's **energy** is **proportional** to its **temperature** (see page 39).

1) The Kelvin scale is named after Lord Kelvin who first suggested it.
2) A change of **1 K** equals a change of **1 °C**.
3) To change from degrees Celsius into kelvin you **add 273** (or 273.15 if you need to be really precise).

$$K = C + 273$$

All equations in **thermal physics** use temperatures measured in kelvin.

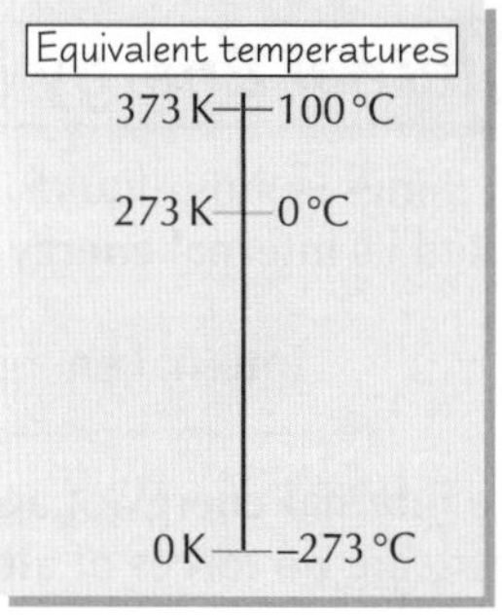

It's true. –273.15 °C is the lowest temperature theoretically possible. Weird, huh. You'd kinda think there wouldn't be a minimum, but there is.

Pressure and Volume are Proportional to Temperature

The relationships between the **temperature**, **pressure** and **volume** of a **gas** were worked out separately through careful **experimentation**. Each relationship applies to a **fixed mass** of gas.

An ideal gas obeys the relationships exactly.

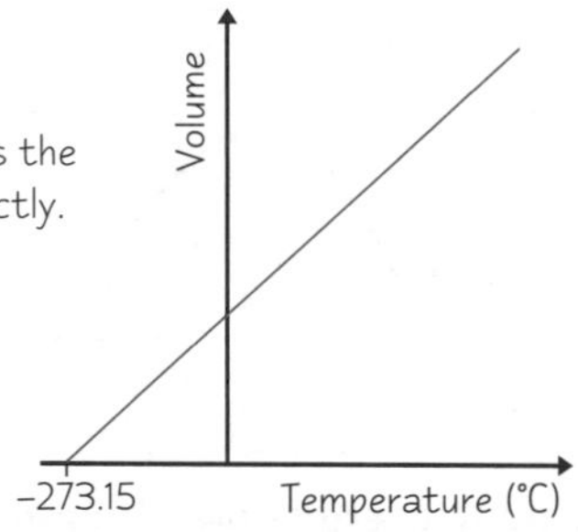

An ideal gas is a good approximation for a real gas at low pressure and fairly high temperature.

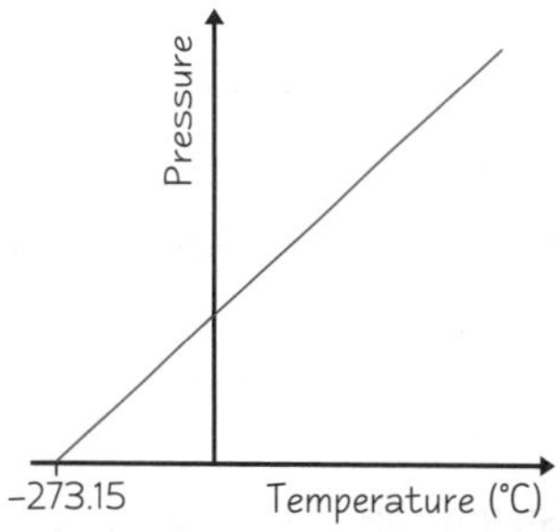

At constant **pressure**, the **volume** V of a gas is **directly proportional** to its **absolute temperature** T.

At constant **volume**, the **pressure** p of a gas is **directly proportional** to its **absolute temperature** T.

You can **combine** these relationships to form an equation — called the **equation of state for an ideal gas.**

$pV = NkT$ — *the equation of state*

p is the **pressure** of the gas, V is the **volume**, N is the **number of particles** in the gas, and k is **Boltzmann's constant** with a value of $\mathbf{1.38 \times 10^{-23}\ JK^{-1}}$.

Practice Questions

Q1 Define specific heat capacity.

Q2 Describe how you would measure the specific heat capacity of olive oil.

Q3 Show that the thermal energy needed to heat 2 kg of water from 20 °C to 50 °C is ~250 kJ (c_{water} = 4180 $Jkg^{-1}K^{-1}$).

Q4 What is the equation of state of an ideal gas?

Exam Questions

Q1 A 2 kg metal cylinder is heated uniformly from 4.5 °C to 12.7 °C in 3 minutes.
The electric heater used is rated at 12 V, 7.5 A.
Assuming that heat losses were negligible, calculate the specific heat capacity of the metal. [3 marks]

Q2 A large helium balloon has a volume of 10 m^3 at ground level. The temperature of the gas in the balloon is 293 K and the pressure is 1×10^5 Pa. The balloon is released and rises to a height where its volume becomes 25 m^3 and its temperature is 260 K. Calculate the pressure inside the balloon at its new height. Assume that the number of molecules of gas inside the balloon remains constant. [3 marks]

My specific eat capacity — 24 pies...

*This stuff's a bit dull, but hey... make sure you're comfortable using those equations. Interesting(ish) fact for the day — it's the **huge** difference in specific heat capacity between the land and the sea that causes the monsoon in Asia. So there.*

Internal Energy

The energy of a particle depends on its temperature on the ***thermodynamic scale*** *(that's Kelvin to you and me).*

Internal Energy is the Sum of Kinetic and Potential Energy

All things (solids, liquids, gases) have **energy** contained within them. The amount of **energy** contained in a system is called its **internal energy** — it's found by **summing** the **kinetic** and **potential energy** of all the **particles** within it.

Internal energy is the **sum** of the **kinetic** and **potential energy** of the **particles** within a system.

The **internal energy** of an **ideal gas** is only due to the **kinetic energy** of the **particles** within it.
There are **no forces of attraction** between the particles of an ideal gas, so they **do not** have any **potential energy**.

The Speed Distribution of Gas Particles Depends on Temperature

The **particles** in a **gas don't** all **travel** at the **same speed**.
Some particles will be moving fast but others much more slowly.
Most will travel around the average speed. The shape of the **speed distribution** depends on the **temperature** of the gas.

As the temperature of the gas increases:
1) the **average** particle speed increases.
2) the **maximum** particle speed increases.
3) the distribution curve becomes more **spread out**.

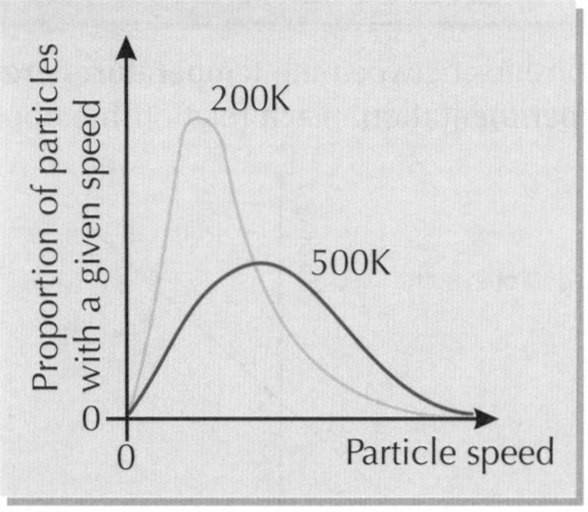

The **random distribution** of the **speed** of gas particles means that their **kinetic energies** are also **randomly distributed**.
And because the **distribution** of the speeds **depends on the temperature**, the **kinetic energy distribution** does too.

Energy Changes Happen Between Particles

The particles of a gas **collide** with each other **all the time**. Some of these collisions will be '**head-on**' (particles moving in **opposite directions**) while others will be '**shunts from behind**' (particles moving in the **same direction**).

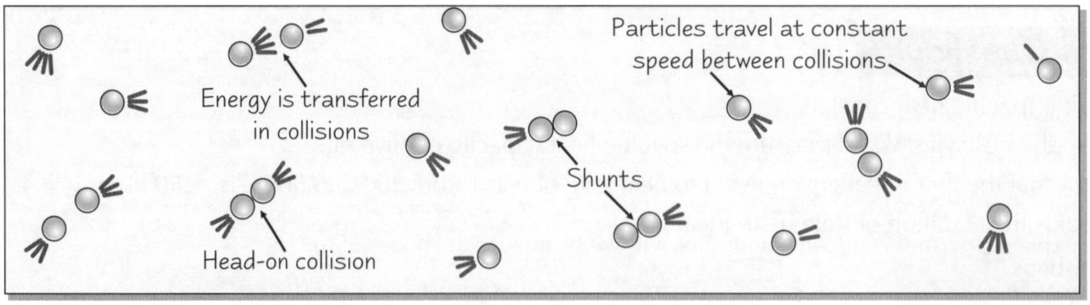

1) As a result of the collisions, **energy** will be **transferred** between particles.
2) Some particles will **gain speed** in a collision and others will **slow down**.
3) **Between collisions**, the particles will travel at **constant speed**.
4) Although the energy of an individual particle changes at each collision, the collisions **don't alter** the **total energy** of the **system**.
5) So, the **average** speed of the particles will stay the same provided the **temperature** of the gas **stays the same**.

Kayleigh tried to explain kinetic theory — but her friends thought it was just a load of balls.

Internal Energy

The Kinetic Energy of Gas Particles is Random

The **kinetic energy** of the particles in a gas is **randomly distributed** and constantly **changing** in collisions. So it doesn't mean much to talk about the **kinetic energy** of an **individual** particle — it's much more useful to estimate the **average kinetic energy** of a particle.

$\frac{1}{2}m\overline{c^2}$ is the **average kinetic energy** of a **gas particle**

In the equation, ***m*** is the **mass** of one particle in the gas and $\overline{c^2}$ stands for the **mean square speed**. The mean square speed is the **average of the squared speeds** of all the particles in the gas. It represents the squared speed of a **typical particle**.

Average Kinetic Energy is Proportional to Absolute Temperature

The graph on the previous page shows how the **speed distribution** of gas particles **depends** on the **temperature**. The **average kinetic energy** of the particles also **depends** on the **temperature**, as shown by the equation below.

$$\frac{1}{2}m\overline{c^2} = \frac{3}{2}kT$$

where ***m*** is the **mass** of one particle in the gas, $\overline{c^2}$ is the **mean square speed**, ***k*** is **Boltzmann's constant** (1.38×10^{-23} JK^{-1}), and ***T*** is the **absolute temperature**.

The **average kinetic energy** is directly proportional to the **absolute temperature**, so the **internal energy** must also be **dependent** on the **temperature** — a **rise** in the **absolute temperature** will cause an **increase** in the kinetic energy of each particle, meaning a rise in **internal energy**.

Practice Questions

Q1 Describe the changes in the distribution of gas particle speeds as the temperature of a gas increases.

Q2 What is internal energy?

Q3 What would cause a rise in internal energy?

Q4 What happens to the average kinetic energy of a particle if the temperature of a gas doubles?

Exam Questions

Q1 The mass of one mole of nitrogen molecules is 2.8×10^{-2} kg. There are 6.02×10^{23} molecules in one mole.

(a) What is the mass of one molecule? [1 mark]

(b) Calculate the typical speed of a nitrogen molecule at 300 K. [3 marks]

(c) Explain why all the nitrogen molecules will not be moving at this speed. [2 marks]

Q2 Some air freshener is sprayed at one end of a room. The room is 8.0 m long and the temperature is 20 °C.

(a) Assuming the average freshener molecule moves at 400 ms^{-1}, how long would it take for a particle to travel directly to the other end of the room? [1 mark]

(b) The perfume from the air freshener only slowly diffuses from one end of the room to the other. Explain why this takes much longer than suggested by your answer to part (a). [2 marks]

(c) How would the speed of diffusion be different if the temperature was 30 °C? Explain your answer. [3 marks]

Positivise your internal energy, man...

Phew... there's a lot to take in on these pages. Go back over it, step by step, and make sure you understand it all: the internal energy, average kinetic energy of the particles in a gas, Boltzmann's constant and the mean square speed.

Radioactive Emissions

You should recognise most of this stuff from GCSE — but that doesn't mean you can skip it. Make sure you know it.

Unstable Atoms are Radioactive

1) If an atom is **unstable**, it will **break down** to **become** more stable. This **instability** could be caused by having **too many neutrons**, **not enough neutrons**, or just **too much energy** in the nucleus.
2) The atom **decays** by **releasing energy** and/or **particles**, until it reaches a **stable form** — this is called **radioactive decay**.
3) Radioactivity is **random** — it can't be predicted.

You Need to Know Three Types of Nuclear Radiation

Learn this table:

Radiation	Symbol	Constituent	Relative Charge	Mass (u)
Alpha	α	A helium nucleus — 2 protons & 2 neutrons	+2	4
Beta-minus (Beta)	β or β^-	Electron	-1	(negligible)
Gamma	γ	Short-wavelength, high-frequency electromagnetic wave.	0	0

u stands for atomic mass unit — see p 23.

The Different Types of Radiation have Different Penetrations

When a radioactive particle **hits** an **atom** it can **knock off electrons**, creating an **ion** — so, **radioactive emissions** are also known as **ionising radiation**.

Alpha, **beta** and **gamma** radiation can be **fired** at a **variety of objects** with **detectors** placed the **other side** to see whether they **penetrate** the object.

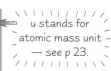

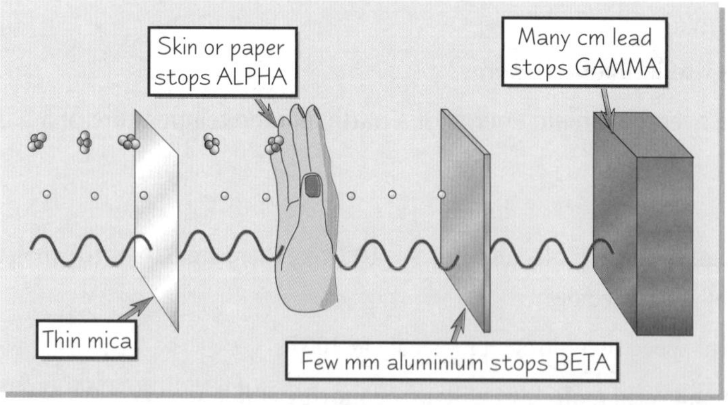

Radiation	Symbol	Ionising	Speed	Penetrating power	Affected by magnetic field
Alpha	α	Strongly	Slow	Absorbed by paper or a few cm of air	Yes
Beta-minus (Beta)	β or β^-	Weakly	Fast	Absorbed by ~3 mm of aluminium	Yes
Gamma	γ	Very weakly	Speed of light	Absorbed by many cm of lead, or several m of concrete.	No

Radioactive Emissions

Alpha and *Beta* Particles have *Different Ionising Properties*

What a **radioactive source** can be **used** for often depends on its **ionising properties**.

1) **Alpha** particles are **strongly positive** — so they can **easily pull electrons** off atoms, **ionising** them.
2) Ionising an atom **transfers** some of the **energy** from the **alpha particle** to the **atom**. The alpha particle **quickly ionises** many atoms (about 10 000 ionisations per alpha particle) and **loses** all its **energy**. This makes alpha-sources suitable for use in **smoke alarms** because they allow **current** to flow, but won't **travel very far**.
3) The **beta**-minus particle has **lower mass** and **charge** than the alpha particle, but a **higher speed**. This means it can still **knock electrons** off atoms. Each **beta** particle will ionise about 100 atoms, **losing energy** at each interaction.
4) This **lower** number of **interactions** means that beta radiation causes much **less damage** to body tissue than alpha radiation. This means beta radiation can be used in **medicine** to target and damage **cancerous cells** — since it passes through healthy tissue without causing too many problems.
5) Gamma radiation is even more **weakly ionising** than beta radiation, so will do even **less damage** to body tissue. This means it can be used for **diagnostic techniques** in medicine.

We're *Surrounded* by *Background Radiation*

Put a Geiger-Müller tube **anywhere** and the counter will click — it's detecting **background radiation**.
There are many **sources** of background radiation:

1) **The air:** Radioactive **radon gas** is released from **rocks**. It emits alpha radiation. The concentration of this gas in the atmosphere varies a lot from place to place, but it's usually the largest contributor to the background radiation.
2) **The ground and buildings: All rock** contains radioactive isotopes.
3) **Cosmic radiation:** Cosmic rays are particles (mostly high-energy protons) from **space**. When they collide with particles in the upper atmosphere, they produce nuclear radiation.
4) **Living things:** All plants and animals contain **carbon**, and some of this will be the radioactive isotope **carbon-14**.
5) **Man-made radiation:** In most areas, radiation from **medical** or **industrial** sources makes up a tiny, tiny fraction of the background radiation.

When you take a **reading** from a radioactive source, you need to **measure** the **background radiation** separately and **subtract** it from your **measurement**.

Practice Questions

Q1 What makes an atom radioactive?

Q2 Name three types of nuclear radiation and give three properties of each.

Q3 Describe the differences in ionising and penetrating powers of the three main types of nuclear radiation.

Q4 Give three sources of background radiation.

Exam Question

Q1 Briefly describe an absorption experiment to distinguish between alpha, beta and gamma radiation.
You may wish to include a sketch in your answer. [4 marks]

Radioactive emissions — as easy as α, β, γ...

You need to learn the different types of radiation and their properties. Remember that alpha particles are by far the most ionising and so cause more damage to body tissue than the same dose of any other radiation — which is one reason we don't use alpha sources as medical tracers. Learn this all really well, then go and have a brew and a bickie...

Exponential Law of Decay

Oooh look — some maths. Good.

Every Isotope Decays at a Different Rate

1) **Radioactive decay** is completely **random**. You **can't predict which** atom will decay **when**.

2) Although you can't predict the decay of an **individual atom**, if you take a **very large number of atoms**, their **overall behaviour** shows a **pattern**.

3) Any sample of a particular **isotope** has the **same rate of decay**, i.e. the same **proportion** of atoms will **decay** in a **given time**.

It could be you.

The Rate of Decay is Measured by the Decay Constant

The **activity** of a sample — the **number** of atoms that **decay each second** — is **proportional** to the **size of the sample**. For a **given isotope**, a sample **twice** as big would give **twice** the **number of decays** per second.

The **decay constant** (λ) measures how **quickly** an isotope will **decay** — the **bigger** the value of λ, the faster the rate of decay. Its unit is s^{-1}.

> activity = decay constant × number of atoms

Or in symbols: $A = \lambda N$ ← Don't get λ confused with wavelength.

Activity is measured in **becquerels** (Bq): 1 Bq = 1 decay per second (s^{-1})

You Need to Learn the Definition of Half-Life

> The **half-life** ($T_{\frac{1}{2}}$) of an **isotope** is the **average time** it takes for the **number of undecayed atoms** to **halve**.

Measuring the **number of undecayed atoms** isn't the easiest job in the world. **In practice**, half-life isn't measured by counting atoms, but by measuring the **time it takes** the **activity** to **halve**.

The **longer** the **half-life** of an isotope, the **longer** it stays **radioactive**.

The **decay constant** and **half-life** are related by the equation: ⟶

(where ln is the natural log)

$$\lambda = \frac{\ln 2}{T_{\frac{1}{2}}} \simeq \frac{0.693}{T_{\frac{1}{2}}}$$

The Number of Undecayed Particles Decreases Exponentially

The half-life stays the same. It takes the same amount of time for half of the atoms to decay regardless of the number of atoms you start with.

The number of atoms approaches zero.

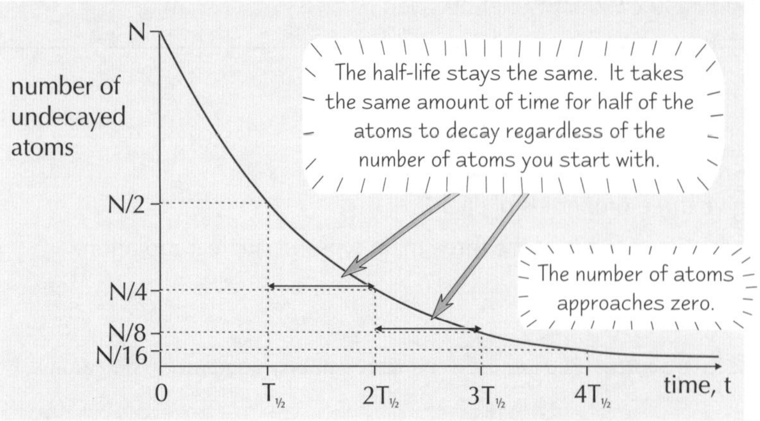

You'd be **more likely** to actually meet a **count rate-time graph** or an **activity-time graph**. They're both **exactly the same shape** as the graph above, but with different **y-axes**.

When you're **measuring** the **activity** and **half-life** of a source, you've got to **remember background radiation**. The **background radiation** needs to be **subtracted** from the **activity readings** to give the **source activity**.

How to find the half-life of an isotope

STEP 1: Read off the value of count rate, particles or activity when t = 0.

STEP 2: Go to half the original value.

STEP 3: Draw a horizontal line to the curve, then a vertical line down to the x-axis.

STEP 4: Read off the half-life where the line crosses the x-axis.

STEP 5: Check the units carefully.

STEP 6: It's always a good idea to check your answer. Repeat steps 1-4 for a quarter the original value. Divide your answer by two. That will also give you the half-life. Check that you get the same answer both ways.

Exponential Law of Decay

You Need to Know the Equations for Decay...

1) The rate of radioactive decay is proportional to the number of nuclei remaining — you can write this as a **differential equation**.

$$\frac{dN}{dt} = -\lambda N$$

The solution to this beauty is the exponential function below.

2) The **number of radioactive atoms** remaining, N, depends on the **number originally** present, N_o. The **number remaining** can be calculated using the equation:

$$N = N_0 e^{-\lambda t}$$

Here t = time, measured in seconds.

You've got to be able to **rearrange** this equation for t — and that means playing with logs:

$$N = N_0 e^{-\lambda t}$$
$$\ln N = \ln N_0 - \lambda t$$
$$\ln\left(\frac{N}{N_0}\right) = -\lambda t$$

(see p62 for more on logs)

Example:
A sample of the radioactive isotope ^{13}N contains 5×10^6 atoms. The decay constant for this isotope is 1.16×10^{-3} s^{-1}.

a) What is the half-life for this isotope?

$$\lambda = \frac{\ln 2}{T_{\frac{1}{2}}} \Rightarrow T_{\frac{1}{2}} = \frac{\ln 2}{\lambda} = \frac{\ln 2}{1.16 \times 10^{-3}} = 598 \text{ s}$$

b) How many atoms of ^{13}N will remain after 800 seconds?

$$N = N_0 e^{-\lambda t} = 5 \times 10^6 e^{-(1.16 \times 10^{-3})(800)} = 1.98 \times 10^6 \text{ atoms}$$

Radioactive Isotopes Have Many Uses

1) Radioactive substances are extremely useful. You can use them for all sorts — e.g. to diagnose and treat **medical problems**, **sterilise** food, and in **smoke alarms**.
2) Carbon-14 is used in **radiocarbon dating**. Living plants take in carbon dioxide from the atmosphere, including the **radioactive isotope carbon-14**. When they **die**, the **activity** of carbon-14 starts to **fall** with a **half-life** of around **5730 years**. By measuring the activity of a sample, you can **date** objects made from once-living material.
3) But radioactive isotopes can cause **serious health problems** if they're not handled properly (see p41), and some isotopes stay radioactive for **thousands** of years.

Practice Questions

Q1 Define radioactive activity. What units is it measured in?

Q2 Sketch a general radioactive decay graph showing the number of undecayed particles against time.

Q3 What is meant by the term 'half-life'?

Q4 Describe how radiocarbon dating works.

Exam Questions

Q1 'Radioactive decay is a random process.' This statement means that:

A You can predict the exact number of atoms that will decay, but not which ones.
B You can't estimate the fraction of atoms that will decay in a given time.
C You can't predict when an atom will decay — you can only estimate the proportion that will decay in a given time.
D You can't make any calculations about the decay of a sample. [1 mark]

Q2 You take a reading of 750 Bq from a pure radioactive source. The radioactive source initially contains 50 000 atoms, and background activity in your lab is measured as 50 Bq.

(a) Calculate the decay constant for your sample. [3 marks]
(b) What is the half-life of this sample? [2 marks]
(c) Approximately how many atoms of the radioactive source will there be after 300 seconds? [2 marks]

Radioactivity is a random process — just like revision shouldn't be...

Remember the shape of that graph — whether it's count rate, activity or number of atoms plotted against time, the shape's always the same. This is all pretty straightforward mathsy-type stuff: plugging values in equations, reading off graphs, etc. Not very interesting, though. But then, in the immortal words of my mate Sarah, you can't have a tick in every box...

Simple Harmonic Motion

Something simple at last — I like the sound of this. And colourful graphs too — you're in for a treat here.

SHM is Defined in terms of Acceleration and Displacement

1) An object moving with **simple harmonic motion** (SHM) **oscillates** to and fro, either side of a **midpoint**.
2) The distance of the object from the midpoint is called its **displacement**.
3) There is always a **restoring force** pulling or pushing the object back **towards** the **midpoint**.
4) The **size** of the **restoring force** depends on the **displacement**, and the force makes the object **accelerate** towards the midpoint:

> **SHM:** an oscillation in which the **acceleration** of an object is **directly proportional** to its **displacement** from the **midpoint**, and is directed **towards the midpoint**.

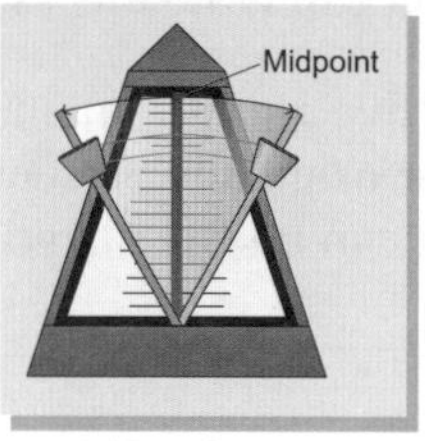

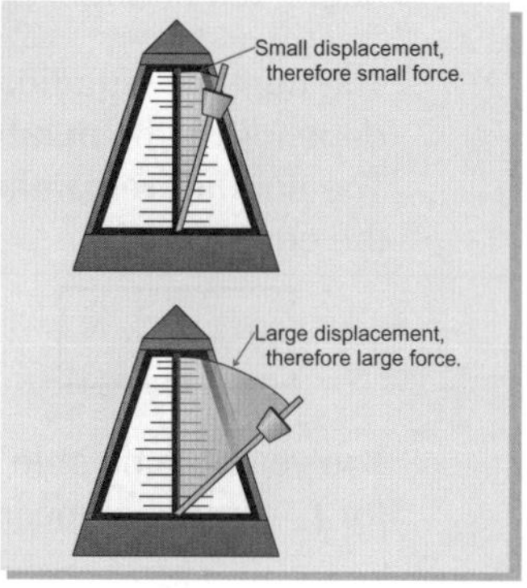

The Restoring Force makes the Object Exchange PE and KE

1) The **type** of **potential energy** (PE) depends on **what it is** that's providing the **restoring force**. This will be **gravitational PE** for pendulums and **elastic PE** (elastic stored energy) for masses on springs.
2) As the object moves **towards the midpoint**, the restoring force **does work** on the object and so **transfers** some **PE** to **KE**. When the object is moving **away from the midpoint**, all that KE is transferred **back to PE** again.
3) At the **midpoint**, the object's **PE** is **zero** and its **KE** is **maximum**.
4) At the **maximum displacement** (the **amplitude**) on both sides of the midpoint, the object's **KE** is **zero** and its **PE** is **maximum**.

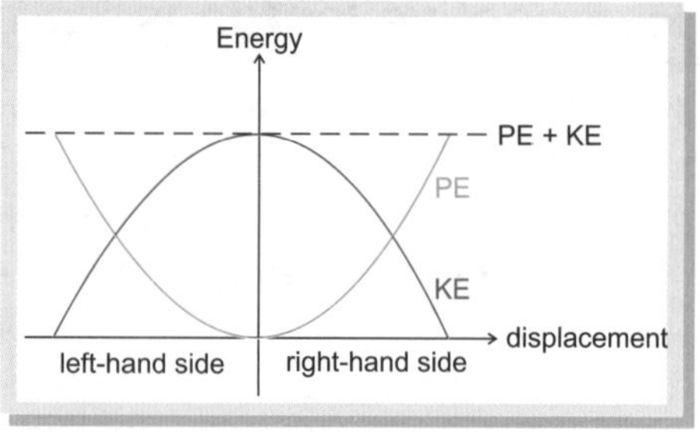

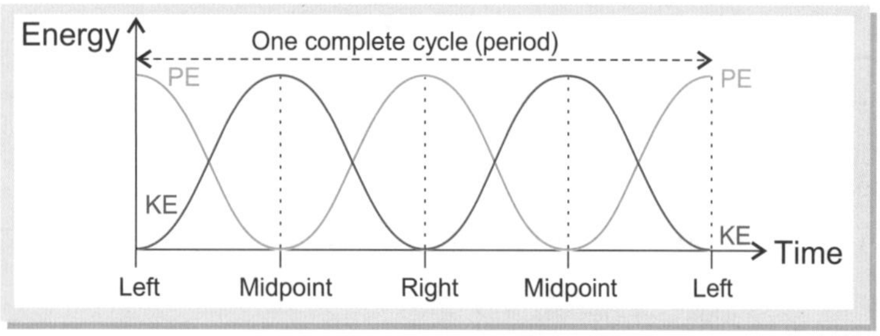

5) The **sum** of the **potential** and **kinetic** energy is called the **mechanical energy** and **stays constant** (as long as the motion isn't damped — see p. 48-49).
6) The **energy transfer** for one complete cycle of oscillation (see graph) is: PE to KE to PE to KE to PE ... and then the process repeats...

You can Draw Graphs to Show Displacement, Velocity and Acceleration

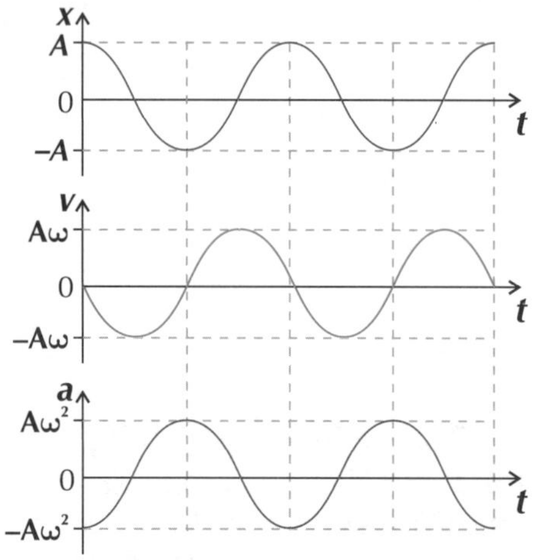

Displacement, ***x***, varies as a cosine or sine wave with a maximum value, ***A*** (the amplitude).

Velocity, ***v***, is the gradient of the displacement-time graph. It has a maximum value of $A\omega$ (where ω is the angular speed) and is a quarter of a cycle in front of the displacement.

Acceleration, ***a***, is the gradient of the velocity-time graph. It has a maximum value of $A\omega^2$, and is in antiphase with the displacement.

Simple Harmonic Motion

The **Frequency** and **Period** don't depend on the **Amplitude**

1) From **maximum positive displacement** (e.g. maximum displacement to the right) to **maximum negative displacement** (e.g. maximum displacement to the left) and **back again** is called a **cycle** of oscillation.
2) The **frequency**, ***f***, of the SHM is the number of cycles per second (measured in Hz).
3) The **period**, ***T***, is the **time** taken for a complete cycle (in seconds).

In SHM, the **frequency** and **period** are independent of the **amplitude** (i.e. constant for a given oscillation). So a pendulum clock will keep ticking in regular time intervals even if its swing becomes very small.

Learn the SHM Equations

I know it looks like there are loads of complicated equations to learn here, but don't panic — it's not that bad really. You'll be given these formulas in the exam, so just make sure you know what they mean and how to use them.

1) According to the definition of SHM, the **acceleration**, ***a***, is directly proportional to the **displacement**, ***x***. The **constant of proportionality** depends on the **frequency**, and the acceleration is always in the **opposite direction** from the displacement (so there's a minus sign in the equation).

$$a = -\omega^2 x \qquad a = -A\omega^2 \cos(\omega t)$$

Don't forget, A is the maximum displacement — it's not acceleration.

Jeremy was investigating swinging as a form of simple harmonic motion.

2) The **velocity** is **positive** when the object's moving in one direction, and **negative** when it's moving in the opposite direction. For example, a **pendulum's velocity** is **positive** when it's moving from **left to right** and **negative** when it's moving from **right to left**.

$$v = -A\omega \sin(\omega t)$$

3) The **displacement** varies with time according to the equation on the right. To use this equation you need to start timing when the pendulum is at its **maximum displacement** — i.e. when $t = 0$, $x = A$.

$$x = A\cos(\omega t)$$

Practice Questions

Q1 Sketch a graph of how the velocity of an object oscillating with SHM varies with time.
Q2 What is the special relationship between the acceleration and the displacement in SHM?
Q3 Given the amplitude and the frequency, how would you work out the maximum acceleration?

Exam Questions

Q1 (a) Define *simple harmonic motion*. [2 marks]

(b) Explain why the motion of a ball bouncing off the ground is not SHM. [1 mark]

Q2 A pendulum is pulled a distance 0.05 m from its midpoint and released.
It oscillates with simple harmonic motion with a frequency of 1.5 Hz. Calculate:

(a) its maximum velocity [1 mark]

(b) its displacement 0.1 s after it is released [2 marks]

(c) the time it takes to fall to 0.01 m from the midpoint after it is released [2 marks]

"Simple" harmonic motion — hmmm, I'm not convinced...

The basic concept of SHM is simple enough (no pun intended). Make sure you can remember the shapes of all the graphs on page 44 and the equations from this page, then just get as much practice at using the equations as you can.

Simple Harmonic Oscillators

There are a couple more equations to learn on this page I'm afraid. The experiment described on this page shows where they come from, though, so that should help you remember them.

A Mass on a Spring is a Simple Harmonic Oscillator (SHO)

1) When the mass is **pushed to the left** or **pulled to the right** of the **equilibrium position**, there's a **force** exerted on it.

2) The size of this force is:

$$F = -kx$$

where k is the **spring constant** (stiffness) of the spring in Nm^{-1} and x is the displacement in m.

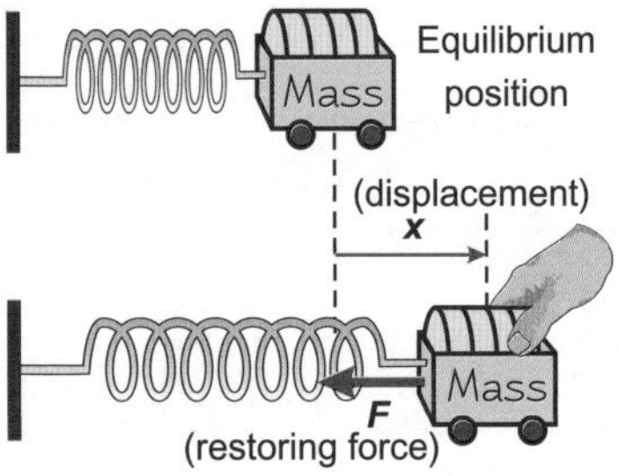

3) After a bit of jiggery-pokery involving Newton's second law and some of the ideas on the previous page, you get the **formula for the period of a mass oscillating on a spring**:

$$T = 2\pi\sqrt{\frac{m}{k}}$$

where T = period of oscillation in seconds
m = mass in kg
k = spring constant in Nm^{-1}

A simple theory of how atoms in a lattice (i.e. a solid) behave can be worked out by considering them as masses oscillating on springs. So there you go.

You Can Check the Formula Experimentally

As promised, this experiment shows you where the equations come from.
It's not too tricky — you just have to change **one variable at a time** and see what happens.

Investigating the Mass-Spring System

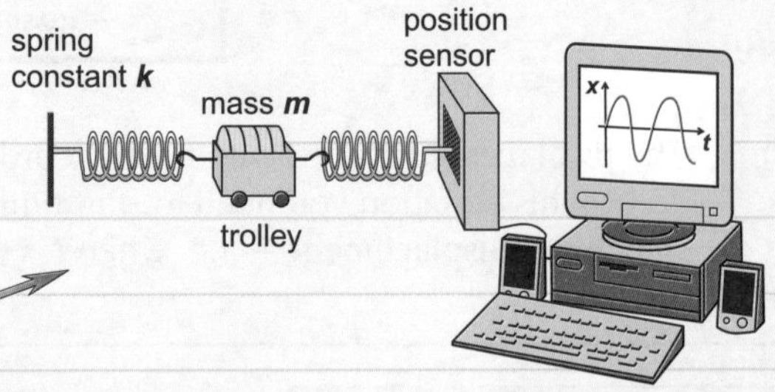

1) You could measure the **period**, T, by getting a computer to plot a **displacement-time graph** from a **data logger**.

2) Attach a **trolley** between two **springs**, pull it to one side by a certain amount and then let go. The trolley will **oscillate** back and forth as the springs pull it in each direction.

3) Change the **mass**, m, by loading the trolley with **masses** — don't forget to include the mass of the trolley in your calculations.

4) Change the **spring stiffness**, k, by using different combinations of springs.

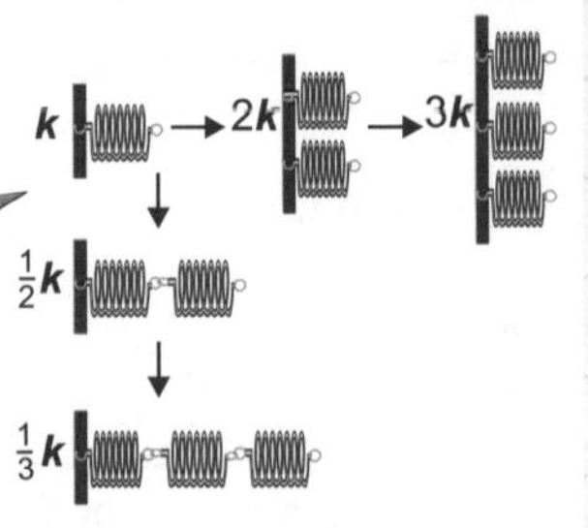

5) Change the **amplitude**, A, by pulling the trolley across by different amounts.

6) You'll get the following **results**: *(∝ means "is proportional to")*

a) $T \propto \sqrt{m}$ so $T^2 \propto m$

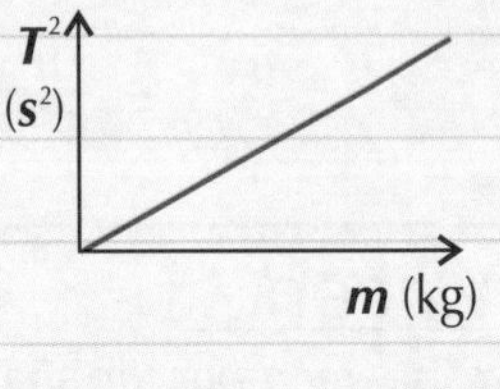

b) $T \propto \sqrt{\frac{1}{k}}$ so $T^2 \propto \frac{1}{k}$

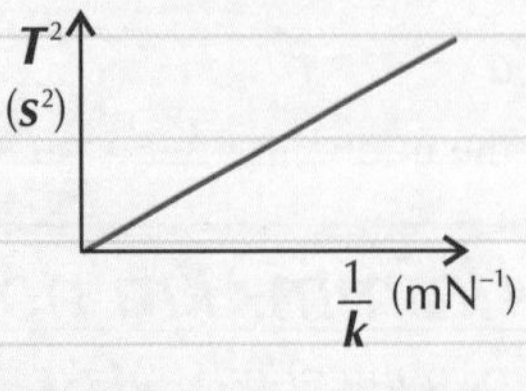

c) T doesn't depend on amplitude, A.

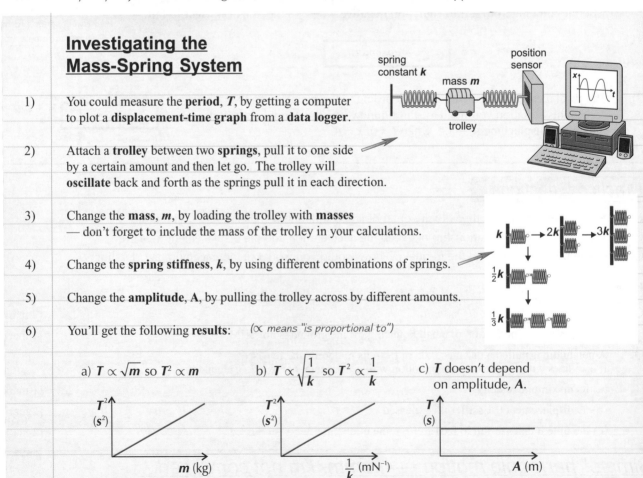

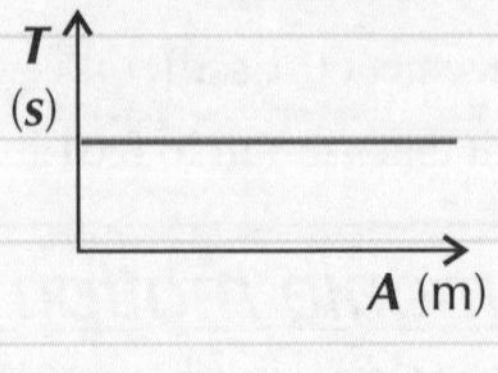

Simple Harmonic Oscillators

The *Simple Pendulum* is the *Classic Example* of an *SHO*

If you set up a simple pendulum attached to an angle sensor and computer like this — then change the length, ***l***, the mass of the bob, ***m***, and the amplitude, ***A***, you get the following results:

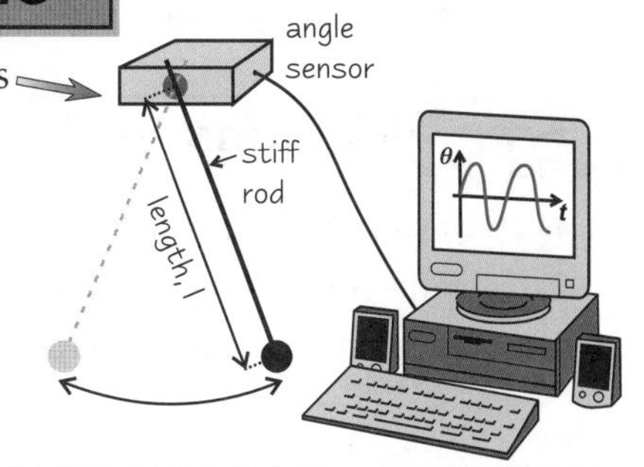

a) $T \propto \sqrt{l}$, so $T^2 \propto l$

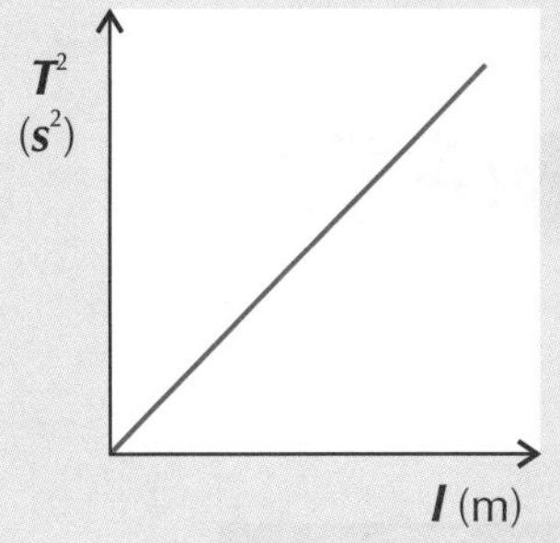

b) ***T*** does not depend on ***m***.

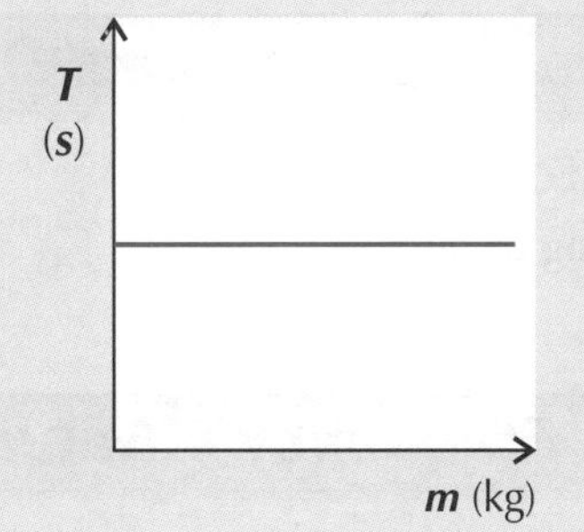

c) ***T*** does not depend on ***A***.

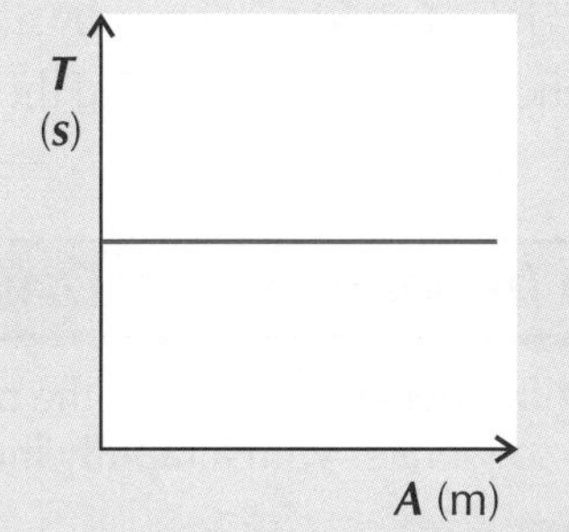

Bob hung around waiting for the experiment to start.

The **formula for the period of a pendulum** is:
(The derivation's quite hard, so you don't need to know it.)
This formula only works for small angles of oscillation — up to about 10° from the equilibrium point.

$$T = 2\pi\sqrt{\frac{l}{g}}$$

where ***T*** = period of oscillation in seconds
l = length of pendulum (between pivot and centre of mass of bob) in m
g = gravitational field strength in Nkg^{-1}

Practice Questions

Q1 Write down the formulae for the period of a mass on a spring and the period of a pendulum.

Q2 Describe a method you could use to measure the period of an oscillator.

Q3 For a mass-spring system, what graphs could you plot to find out how the period depends on: a) the mass, b) the spring constant, and c) the amplitude? What would they look like?

Exam Questions

Q1 A spring of original length 0.10 m is suspended from a stand and clamp.
A mass of 0.10 kg is attached to the bottom and the spring extends to a total length of 0.20 m.

(a) Calculate the spring constant of the spring in Nm^{-1}. ($g = 9.81$ Nkg^{-1}) [2 marks]

The spring isn't moving at this point, so the forces on it must be balanced.

(b) The mass is pulled down a further 2 cm and then released. Assuming the mass oscillates with simple harmonic motion, calculate the period of the subsequent oscillations. [1 mark]

(c) What mass would be needed to make the period of oscillation twice as long? [2 marks]

Q2 Two pendulums of different lengths were released from rest at the top of their swing.
It took exactly the same time for the shorter pendulum to make five complete oscillations as it took the longer pendulum to make three complete oscillations.
The shorter pendulum had a length of 0.20 m. Show that the length of the longer one was 0.56 m. [3 marks]

Go on — SHO the examiners what you're made of...

The most important things to remember on these pages are those two period equations. You'll be given them in your exam, but you need to know what they mean and be happy using them.

Free and Forced Vibrations

Resonance... hmm... tricky little beast. Remember the Millennium Bridge, that standard-bearer of British engineering? The wibbles and wobbles were caused by resonance. How was it sorted out? By damping, which is coming up too.

Free Vibrations — *No Transfer* of *Energy* To or From the *Surroundings*

1) If you stretch and release a mass on a spring, it oscillates at its **natural frequency**.
2) If **no energy's transferred** to or from the surroundings, it will **keep** oscillating with the **same amplitude forever**.
3) In practice this **never happens**, but a spring vibrating in air is called a **free vibration** anyway.

Forced Vibrations happen when there's an *External Driving Force*

1) A system can be **forced** to vibrate by a periodic **external force**.
2) The frequency of this force is called the **driving frequency**.

Resonance happens when *Driving Frequency* = *Natural Frequency*

When the **driving frequency** approaches the **natural frequency**, the system gains more and more energy from the driving force and so vibrates with a **rapidly increasing amplitude**. When this happens the system is **resonating**.

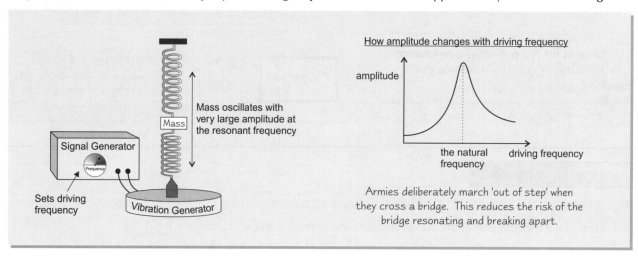

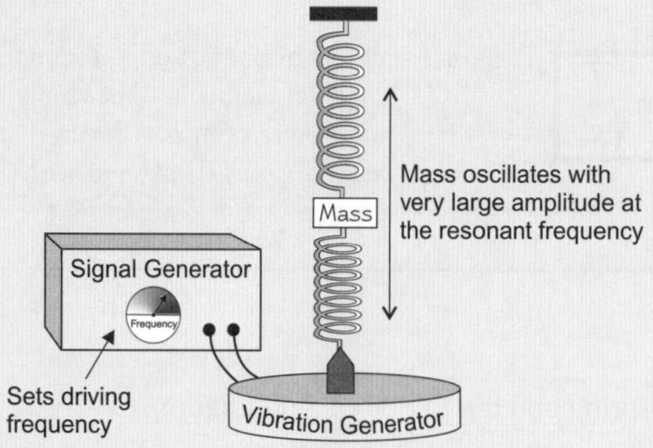

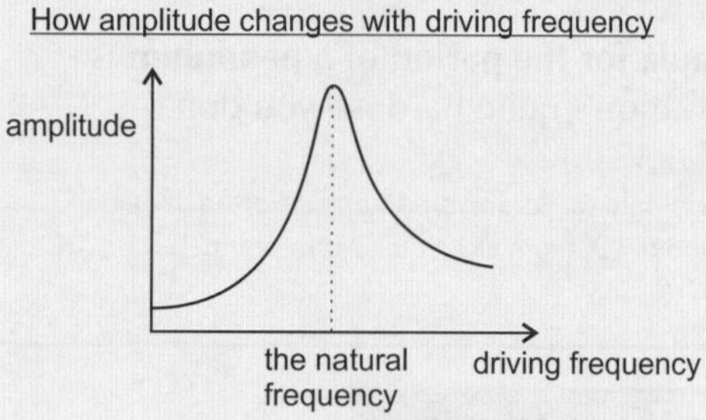

Armies deliberately march 'out of step' when they cross a bridge. This reduces the risk of the bridge resonating and breaking apart.

Examples of resonance:

a) organ pipe

The column of air resonates, driven by the motion of air at the base.

b) swing

A swing resonates if it's driven by someone pushing it at its natural frequency.

c) glass smashing

A glass resonates when driven by a sound wave at the right frequency.

d) radio

A radio is tuned so the electric circuit resonates at the same frequency as the radio station you want to listen to.

Damping happens when *Energy* is *Lost* to the *Surroundings*

1) In practice, **any** oscillating system **loses energy** to its surroundings.
2) This is usually down to **frictional forces** like air resistance.
3) These are called **damping forces**.
4) Systems are often **deliberately damped** to **stop** them oscillating or to **minimise** the effect of **resonance**.

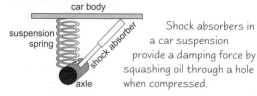

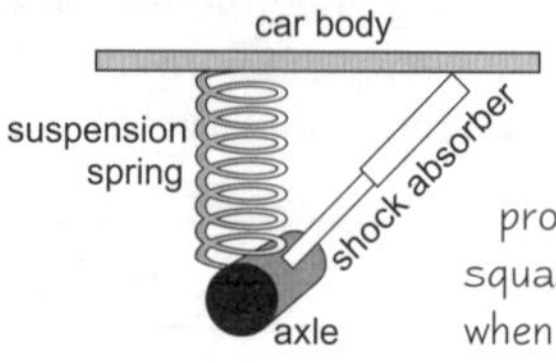

Shock absorbers in a car suspension provide a damping force by squashing oil through a hole when compressed.

Free and Forced Vibrations

Different Amounts of Damping have Different Effects

1) The **degree** of damping can vary from **light** damping (where the damping force is small) to **overdamping**.
2) Damping **reduces** the **amplitude** of the oscillation over time. The **heavier** the damping, the **quicker** the amplitude is reduced to zero.
3) **Critical damping** reduces the amplitude (i.e. stops the system oscillating) in the **shortest possible time**.
4) Car **suspension systems** and moving coil **meters** are critically damped so that they **don't oscillate** but return to equilibrium as quickly as possible.
5) Systems with **even heavier damping** are **overdamped**. They take **longer** to return to equilibrium than a critically damped system.

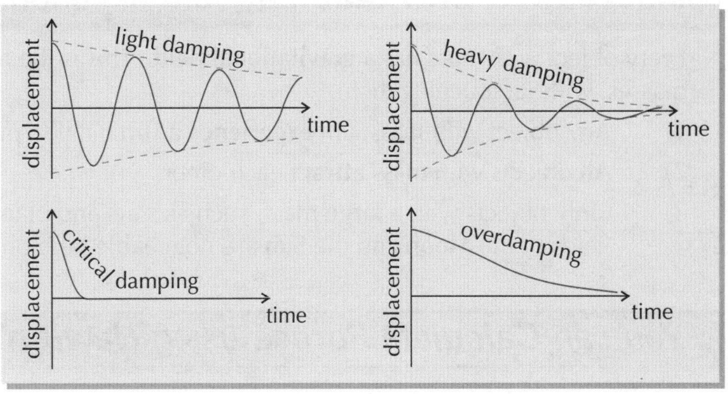

6) **Plastic deformation** of ductile materials **reduces** the **amplitude** of oscillations in the same way as damping. As the material changes shape, it **absorbs energy**, so the oscillation will be smaller.

Damping Affects Resonance too

1) **Lightly damped** systems have a **very sharp** resonance peak. Their amplitude only increases dramatically when the **driving frequency** is **very close** to the **natural frequency**.
2) **Heavily damped** systems have a **flatter response**. Their amplitude doesn't increase very much near the natural frequency and they aren't as **sensitive** to the driving frequency.

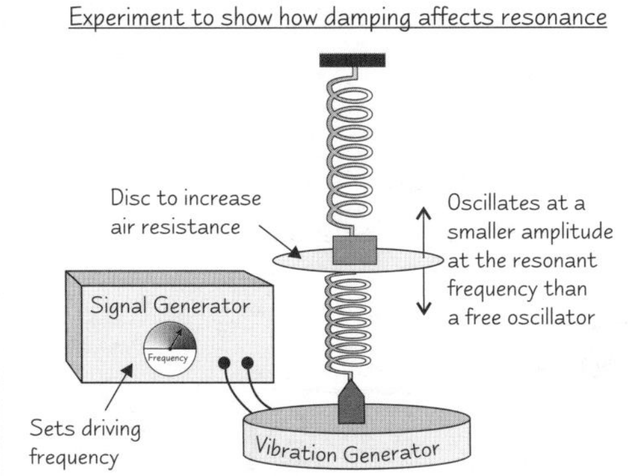

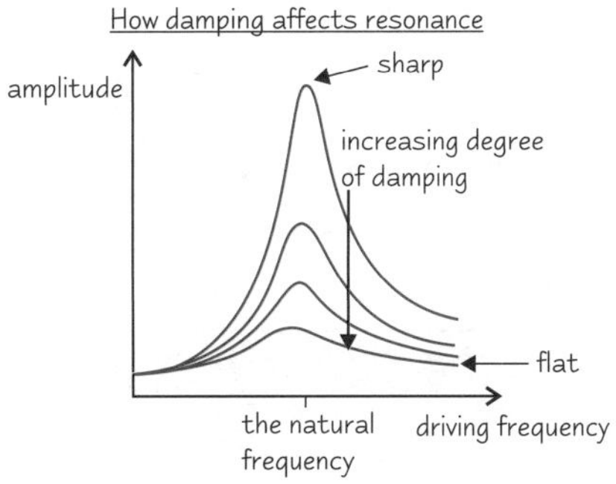

Structures are damped to avoid being damaged by resonance. Loudspeakers are also made to have as flat a response as possible so that they don't 'colour' the sound.

Practice Questions

Q1 What is a free vibration? What is a forced vibration?

Q2 Draw diagrams to show how a damped system oscillates with time when the system is lightly damped and when the system is critically damped.

Exam Questions

Q1 (a) What is resonance? [2 marks]
(b) Draw a diagram to show how the amplitude of a lightly damped system varies with driving frequency. [2 marks]
(c) On the same diagram, show how the amplitude of the system varies with driving frequency when it is heavily damped. [1 mark]

Q2 (a) What is critical damping? [1 mark]
(b) Describe a situation where critical damping is used. [1 mark]

A2 Physics — it can really put a damper on your social life...

Resonance can be really useful (radios, oboes, swings — yay) or very, very bad...

Gravitational Fields

*Gravity's all about masses **attracting** each other. If the Earth didn't have a **gravitational field**, apples wouldn't fall to the ground and you'd probably be floating off into space instead of sitting here reading this page...*

Masses in a Gravitational Field experience a Force of Attraction

Every object with mass has a **gravitational field**. This is the region where it can **exert** an **attractive force** on other masses, without touching them.

1) Any object with mass will **experience a force** if you put it in the **gravitational field** of another object.
2) All objects with mass **attract** each other.
3) Only objects with a **large** mass, such as stars and planets, have a significant effect. E.g. the gravitational fields of the **Moon** and the **Sun** are noticeable here on Earth — they're the main cause of our **tides**.

You can Calculate Forces using Newton's Law of Gravitation

The **force** experienced by an object in a gravitational field is always **attractive**. It's a **vector** which depends on the **masses** involved and the **distances** between them. It's easy to work this out for **point masses** — or objects that behave as if all their mass is concentrated at the centre. You just put the numbers into this equation...

NEWTON'S LAW OF GRAVITATION:

$$F = \frac{Gm_1m_2}{r^2}$$

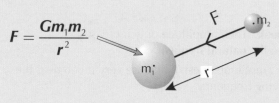

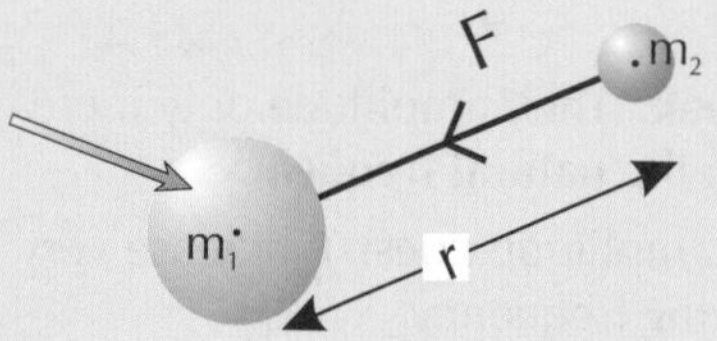

The diagram shows the force acting on m_2 due to m_1. (The force on m_1 due to m_2 is equal but in the opposite direction.)

m_1 and m_2 behave as point masses.

G is the **gravitational constant** — 6.67×10^{-11} Nm²kg⁻².

r is the distance (in metres) between the centres of the two masses.

The law of gravitation is an **inverse square law** $\left(F \propto \frac{1}{r^2}\right)$ so:

1) if the distance r between the masses **increases** then the force F will **decrease**.
2) if the **distance doubles** then the **force** will be one **quarter** the strength of the original force.

The Field Strength is the Force per Unit Mass

Gravitational field strength, g, is the **force per unit mass**. Its value depends on **where you are** in the field. There's a really simple equation for working it out:

$$g = \frac{F}{m}$$

1) F is the force experienced by a mass m when it's placed in the gravitational field. Divide F by m and you get the **force per unit mass**.
2) g is a **vector** quantity, always pointing towards the centre of the mass whose field you're describing.
3) The units of g are **newtons per kilogram** (Nkg^{-1}).

The **value** of g at the **Earth's surface** is approximately **9.81** ms^{-2} (or 9.81 Nkg^{-1}).

In a Radial Field, g is Inversely Proportional to r²

Point masses have **radial** gravitational fields.
The value of g depends on the distance r from the centre of the point mass M...

The force on a point mass m in the gravitational field of a point mass M is $F = \frac{GMm}{r^2}$. So, $g = \frac{F}{m} = \frac{GM\cancel{m}}{\cancel{m}r^2} = \frac{GM}{r^2}$.

And it's an **inverse square law** again — as r **increases**, g **decreases**.

$$g = (-)\frac{GM}{r^2}$$

The minus sign is there to show that gravitational fields always act towards the attracting mass.

Gravitational Fields

There are Similarities between Gravitational and Electric Fields...

1) Both gravitational and electric field strengths are unit forces. Gravitational field strength, ***g***, is **force** per **unit mass**. Electric field strength, ***E***, is **force** per **unit positive charge**.
2) Newton's law of gravitation for the **force** between two point masses is an **inverse square law**. Coulomb's law for the electric **force** between two point charges is also an **inverse square law**. So the strength of both forces goes down rapidly as you get further away from the source of the field.

$$F \propto \frac{1}{r^2}$$

... and some Differences too

Take a look at pages 10-11 for more on electric fields.

1) Gravitational forces are always **attractive**. Electric forces can be either **attractive** or **repulsive**.
2) Objects can be **shielded** from **electric** fields, but not from gravitational fields.
3) The size of an **electric** force depends on the **medium** between the charges, e.g. plastic or air. For gravitational forces, this makes no difference.

Energy is Transferred when a Mass or Charge Moves in a Field

In both gravitational and electrical fields, the energy change of a particle depends only on where the particle **starts** and **finishes**. It **doesn't matter** what **path** it takes to get there.

Example in a Gravitational Field

When you throw a ball up in the air you're **doing work** to move the ball against the attractive force of gravity, and **energy** is **converted** from one form to another. In a **uniform gravitational field**, as at the Earth's surface, the calculations are simple:

1) As the ball rises, it **gains** gravitational **potential energy**: $PE = mg\Delta h$
2) When the ball falls, the gravitational potential energy is converted into **kinetic energy**: $KE = \frac{1}{2}mv^2$
(If there's air resistance some will also be converted to heat.)

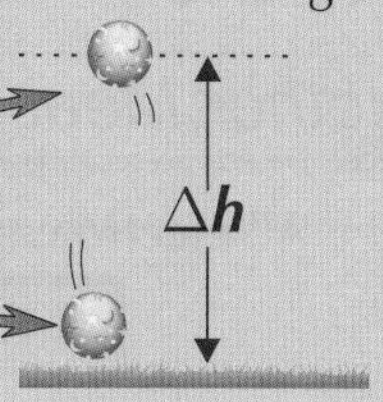

Example in an Electric Field

Two parallel plates have a potential difference of ***V*** across them. This creates a **uniform electric field.**

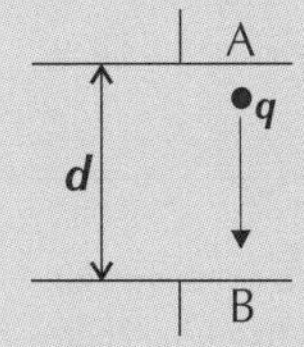

The field strength is $E = \frac{V}{d} = \frac{F}{q}$ which gives $Vq = Fd$

1) To move a charge ***q*** from A to B, the **work done** = **force** × **distance moved** = ***Vq***
2) So the energy needed to move a charge ***q*** against a potential difference ***V*** is given by ***Vq***.

Practice Questions

Q1 Write down Newton's law of gravitation.

Q2 Derive the equation for gravitational field strength from Newton's law of gravitation.

Exam Questions

Q1 The Earth's radius is approximately 6400 km. Estimate its mass (use g = 9.81 Nkg^{-1} at the Earth's surface). [2 marks]

Q2 The Moon has a mass of 7.35×10^{22} kg and a radius of 1740 km. The value of ***g*** at the Moon's surface is:
A 1.62 Nkg^{-1} **B** 2.84 Nkg^{-1} **C** 6.67 Nkg^{-1} **D** 9.84 Nkg^{-1} [1 mark]

If you're really stuck, put 'Inverse Square Law'...

Clever chap, Newton, but famously tetchy. He got into fights with other physicists, mainly over planetary motion and calculus... the usual playground squabbles. Then he spent the rest of his life trying to turn scrap metal into gold. Weird.

Measuring Astronomical Distances

Distances in astronomy are... well, astronomical. Astronomers use some pretty clever techniques to measure them...

Distances and **Velocities** in the Solar System can be Measured using **Radar**

1) **Radio telescopes** can be used to send **short pulses** of **radio waves** towards a planet or asteroid (a rock flying about the Solar System) which **reflect** off the surface and bounce back.
2) The telescope picks up the reflected radio waves, and the **time taken** (***t***) for them to return is measured.
3) Since we know the **speed** of the radio waves (**speed of light, *c***) we can work out the **distance, *d***, to the object using:

$$2d = ct$$

It's 2d, not just d, because the pulse travels twice the distance to the object — there and back again.

4) If **two** short pulses are sent a certain **time interval** apart, you can measure the **distance** an object has moved in that time. From this time and distance, you can calculate the **average speed** of the object **relative** to Earth. More accurate measurements can be made using Doppler shifts (see p.58).

Distances in the Solar System are Often Measured in **Astronomical Units (AU)**

1) From **Copernicus** onwards, astronomers were able to work out the **distance** the **planets** are from the Sun **relative** to the Earth, using **astronomical units** (AU). But they could not work out the **actual distances**.

One **astronomical unit** (AU) is defined as the **mean distance** between the **Earth** and the **Sun**.

2) The **size** of the AU wasn't accurately known until 1769 — when it was carefully **measured** during a **transit of Venus** (when Venus passed between the Earth and the Sun).

Another Measure of Distance is the **Light-Year (ly)**

1) All **electromagnetic waves** travel at the **speed of light, *c***, in a vacuum ($c = 3.00 \times 10^8$ ms^{-1}).

The **distance** that electromagnetic waves travel in **one year** is called a **light-year** (**ly**).

2) If we see the light from a star that is, say, **10 light-years away** then we are actually seeing it as it was **10 years ago**. The further away the object is, the further **back in time** we are actually seeing it.
3) **1 ly** is equivalent to about **63 000 AU**.

The Distance to **Nearby Stars** can be Measured by **Parallax**

1) You experience parallax every day. Imagine you're in a **moving car**. You see that (stationary) objects in the **foreground** seem to be **moving faster** than objects in the **distance**.
2) This **apparent change in position** is called **parallax** and is measured in terms of the **angle of parallax**. The **greater** the **angle**, the **nearer** the object is to you.

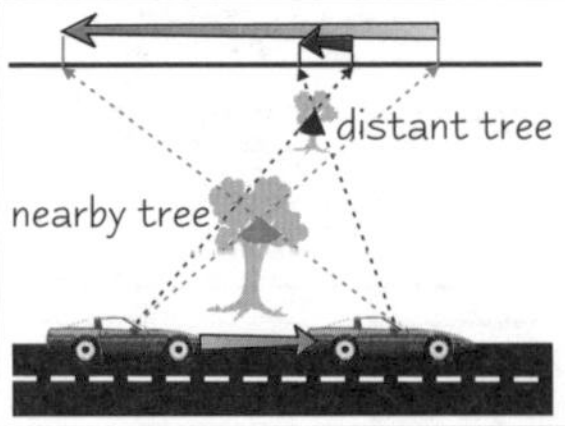

The nearby tree seems to have moved much further relative to the horizon than the more distant tree. The angles marked are called angles of parallax.

3) The distance to **nearby stars** can be calculated by observing how they **move relative** to **very distant stars** when the Earth is in **different parts** of its **orbit**. This gives a **unit** of distance called a **parsec** (**pc**).
4) By knowing the distance between the Sun and the Earth, and measuring the parallax angle, you can use **trigonometry** to work out the distance to a star.

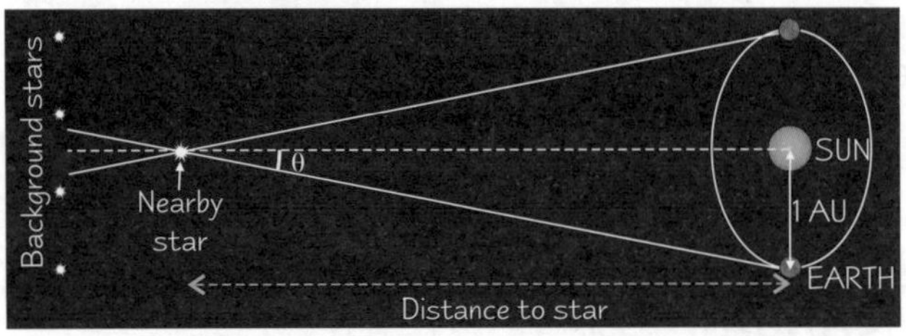

A star is exactly **one parsec** (**pc**) away from Earth if the **angle of parallax**,

$$\theta = \mathbf{1\ arcsecond} = \left(\frac{1}{3600}\right)^\circ$$

5) Parsecs are the distance unit of choice for astronomers, so if you want to be a starry-eyed astrophysicist you'll be seeing a lot more of them.

Measuring Astronomical Distances

The **Luminosity** of a Star Depends on its **Temperature** and **Surface Area**

1) The **luminosity** of a star is the **total energy** it emits **per second**. It's related to the **temperature** of the star and its **surface area**.
2) The luminosity is proportional to the **fourth power** of the star's **temperature** and is **directly proportional** to the **surface area**. This is **Stefan's law**:

$$L = \sigma A T^4$$

where L is the luminosity of the star (in W), A is its surface area (in m^2), T is its surface temperature (in K) and σ (a little Greek "sigma") is Stefan's constant.

3) Measurements give Stefan's constant as $\sigma = 5.67 \times 10^{-8}\ \text{Wm}^{-2}\text{K}^{-4}$.
4) To find the luminosity of a star, remember that stars are **spheres**. You can find the luminosity of a star by substituting the surface area of a sphere, $4\pi r^2$, into Stefan's law:

$$L = 4\pi r^2 \sigma T^4$$

where r is the radius of the star (or sphere).

5) From **Earth**, we can measure the **radiation flux** that reaches us from a star. The flux is the **power** of radiation **per square metre**, so as the radiation spreads out and becomes **diluted**, the flux **decreases**. If the energy has been emitted from a **point** or a **sphere** (like a star, for example) then it obeys the **inverse square law**:

$$F = \frac{L}{4\pi d^2}$$

where L is the luminosity of the star (in W), and d is the distance from the star (in m).

You Can Use **Standard Candles** to Find **Distances** to Galaxies

The distances to most stars and objects in space are **too big** to measure using parallax (see previous page). For these objects you can use **standard candles** to find their distance.

1) Standard candles are objects, such as supernovae and Cepheid variables, that you can calculate the luminosity of **directly**.
2) Because you know the luminosity of the standard candle, you can measure its flux on Earth and use the **inverse square law** to find its distance.
3) So, if you find a standard candle within a galaxy, you can work out how far that galaxy is from us. This is how **Hubble's constant** was worked out (see p. 58).

Practice Questions

Q1 What is meant by the luminosity of a star?

Q2 What is meant by a) an astronomical unit, b) a parsec and c) a light-year?

Q3 What is the relationship between the luminosity, surface area and temperature of a star?

Exam Questions

Q1 Delta Cephei is a standard candle.

(a) What is a standard candle? Describe how you could find the distance to Delta Cephei using its luminosity. [3 marks]

(b) Delta Cephei has a parallax of 3.66×10^{-3} arcseconds.
Describe how you could use this value to calculate the distance to Delta Cephei. [2 marks]

Q2 A star has a luminosity of 3.9×10^{26} W and a surface temperature of 5500 K.
Calculate the surface area of the star. [2 marks]

So — using a ruler's out of the question then...

It's insane to think just how big the Universe is. It's even bigger than this:
Make sure you understand the definition of a parsec — it's a bit of a weird one.

Luminosity and the Hertzsprung-Russell Diagram

Now they're telling us the Sun's black. Who writes this stuff?

*A **Black Body** is a **Perfect Absorber** and **Emitter***

1) Objects emit **electromagnetic radiation** due to their **temperature**. At everyday temperatures this radiation lies mostly in the **infrared** part of the spectrum (which we can't see) — but heat something up enough and it will start to **glow**.
2) **Pure black** surfaces emit radiation **strongly** and in a **well-defined way**. We call it **black body radiation**.
3) A black body is defined as:

> A body that **absorbs all wavelengths** of electromagnetic radiation (that's why it's called a **black** body) and can **emit all wavelengths** of electromagnetic radiation.

4) To a reasonably good approximation **stars** behave as **black bodies** and their black body radiation produces their **continuous spectrum**.
5) The graph of **intensity** against **wavelength** for black body radiation varies with **temperature**, as shown in the graph:

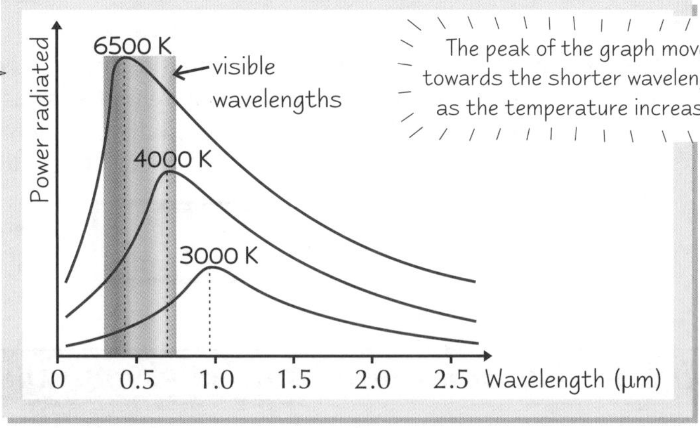

The peak of the graph moves towards the shorter wavelengths as the temperature increases.

*The **Peak Wavelength** gives the **Temperature***

1) For each temperature, there is a **peak** in the black body curve at a wavelength called the **peak wavelength**, λ_{max}.
2) λ_{max} is related to the **temperature** by **Wien's displacement law**:

$$\lambda_{max}T = 2.898 \times 10^{-3}\ \text{m·K}$$

where T is the temperature in kelvin and m·K is a <u>metre-kelvin</u>.

Example The Sun has a surface temperature of 5800 K. Find the peak wavelength of radiation emitted by the Sun.

$$\lambda_{max}T = 2.898 \times 10^{-3}\ \text{m·K}$$

$$\lambda_{max} = \frac{2.898\times10^{-3}\ \text{m.K}}{5800\ \text{K}} \simeq \mathbf{5.0\times10^{-7}\,m}\ (= 500\ \text{nm})$$

*Absorption Spectra — Gases Absorb Particular **Wavelengths***

1) We don't see perfect black body spectra from stars. When we observe light from black bodies like the Sun there are often **dark lines** in the spectrum.
2) This is because the light emitted passes through other gases before being observed. Some wavelengths are **absorbed** by the **electrons** in these gases (to excite them into **higher energy levels**). The dark lines correspond to these **wavelengths**.

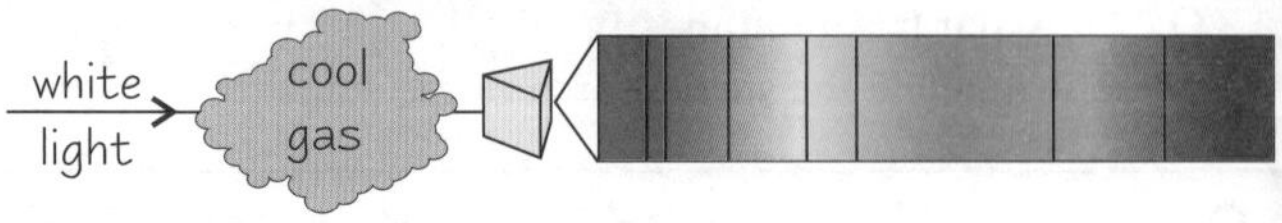

Luminosity and the Hertzsprung-Russell Diagram

Luminosity vs Temperature — the H-R diagram

1) If you plot **luminosity** against **temperature**, you don't just get a random collection of stars. The stars appear to group in **distinct areas** on the plot.

2) The distinct areas show the main stages of a star's life cycle: the **main sequence**, **red giants** and **white dwarfs**. (see the next page for the details). This is called the **Hertzsprung-Russell Diagram.**

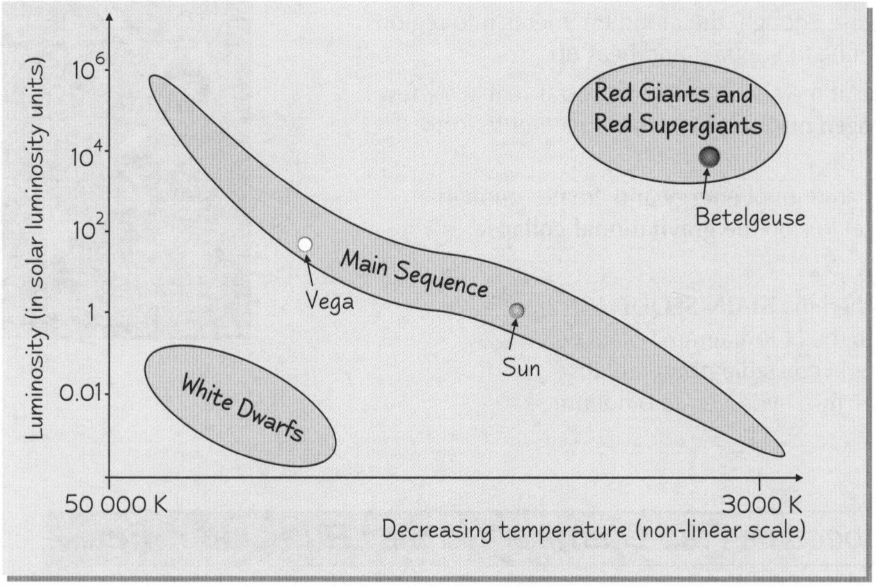

Temperature goes the "wrong way" along the x-axis — from hotter to cooler.

3) The reason you can see these areas is because stars exist in these **stable** stages of their life cycle for **long periods of time**. You don't see groups of stars in any transitional period on the H-R diagram because they are unstable and happen **quickly** (compared with the life of the star).

Practice Questions

Q1 What is Wien's displacement law and what is it used for?

Q2 What is an H-R diagram a plot of?

Q3 What causes dark lines to appear in what would otherwise be a continuous spectrum from the Sun?

Exam Questions

Q1 The star Procyon A produces a black body spectrum with a peak wavelength at 436 nm.
What is the surface temperature of Procyon A to 3 s.f.?
A 6650 K **B** 2900 K **C** 1830 K **D** 7830 K [1 mark]

Q2 A star has a surface temperature of 4000 K and the same luminosity as the Sun (3.9×10^{26} W).

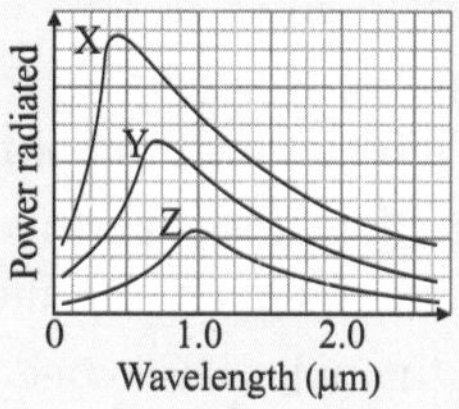

(a) Which radiation curve represents this star — X, Y or Z? Explain your answer. [2 marks]

(b) Calculate the star's surface area. [2 marks]

Q3 Sketch the basic features of an H-R diagram, indicating where you would find main sequence stars, red giants and white dwarfs. [5 marks]

Wavelength to the max...

Who'd have thought something as boring sounding as the H-R diagram could be about the life and times (and deaths) of stars. I know what you're thinking, 'I want to know more about the star life cycle'. Well go on then... just for you...

The Life Cycle of Stars

Stars go through several different stages in their lives and move around the H-R diagram as they go (see p. 55).

Stars Begin as Clouds of Dust and Gas

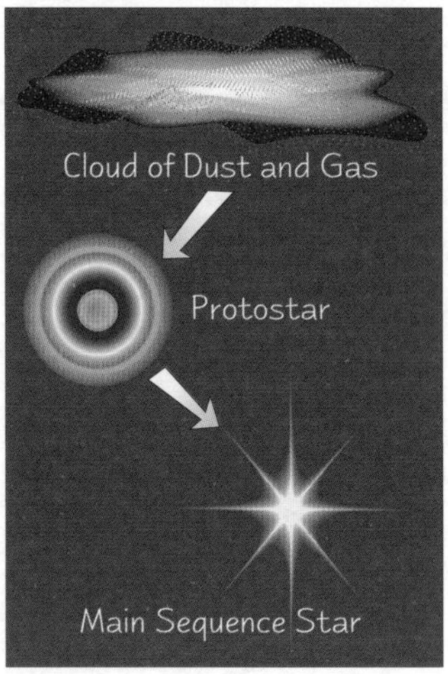

1) Stars are born in a **cloud** of **dust** and **gas**, most of which was left when previous stars blew themselves apart in **supernovae**. The denser clumps of the cloud **contract** (very slowly) under the force of **gravity**.
2) When these clumps get dense enough, the cloud fragments into regions called **protostars** that continue to contract and **heat up**.
3) Eventually the **temperature** at the centre of the protostar reaches a **few million degrees**, and **hydrogen nuclei** start to **fuse** together to form helium (see page 61).
4) This releases an **enormous** amount of **energy** and creates enough **pressure** (radiation pressure) to stop the **gravitational collapse**.

> The star has now reached the **MAIN SEQUENCE**, the **long diagonal band** on the H-R diagram. Stars will stay there in their long-lived **stable phase**, relatively **unchanged**, while they fuse hydrogen into helium.

Main Sequence Stars become Red Giants when they Run Out of Fuel

1) Stars spend most of their lives as **main sequence** stars. While on the main sequence, the **pressure** produced from **hydrogen fusion** (see p.61) in a star's **core balances** the **gravitational force** trying to compress it.
2) When the **hydrogen** in the **core** runs out, nuclear fusion **stops**, and with it the **outward pressure stops**.
3) The core **contracts** and **heats up** under the **weight** of the star until, eventually, it gets **hot** enough and **dense** enough for **helium** to **fuse**.
4) This releases a huge amount of energy which causes the star to expand and become a **RED GIANT** or a **RED SUPERGIANT**.

> When this happens, the star **moves off** the main sequence and to the **top-right** corner of the H-R diagram. Red giants have a **high luminosity** and a relatively **low surface temperature**, so they must have a **huge** surface area because of Stefan's law (page 53).

Low Mass Stars (like the Sun) form White Dwarfs

1) Once all the **helium** in the core of the star is fused, a low mass star will start to collapse again under its own weight.
2) The core of a low mass star won't get up to high enough temperatures for any further **fusion,** and so it'll continue to **contract** under its own **weight**.
3) Once the core has shrunk to about **Earth-size**, **electrons** will exert enough pressure to stop it collapsing any more. This is due to a quantum effect called **electron degeneracy** (fret not — you don't have to know about this).
4) As the core contracts, the outer layers become more and more **unstable**. The star **pulsates** and **ejects** its outer layers into space as a **planetary nebula**, leaving behind the dense core.
5) The star is now a very **hot**, **dense solid** called a **WHITE DWARF**.

> White dwarfs have a **low luminosity** but a **high temperature**, so they must be very **small** (again because of Stefan's law). They lie in the **bottom-left** corner of the H-R diagram. White dwarfs are stars at the **end** of their lives, where all of their fusion reactions have stopped and they are just **slowly cooling down**.

The Life Cycle of Stars

High Mass Stars have a **Shorter Life** and a more **Exciting Death**

1) Even though stars with a **large mass** have a **lot of fuel**, they use it up **more quickly** and don't spend so long as main sequence stars.
2) **Really massive** stars can keep fusing elements until their core is made up of **iron**.
3) Nuclear fusion **beyond iron** isn't **energetically favourable**, though, so once an iron core is formed then very quickly it's goodbye star.
4) The star explodes cataclysmically in a **SUPERNOVA**, leaving behind a **NEUTRON STAR** or (if the star was massive enough) a **BLACK HOLE**.

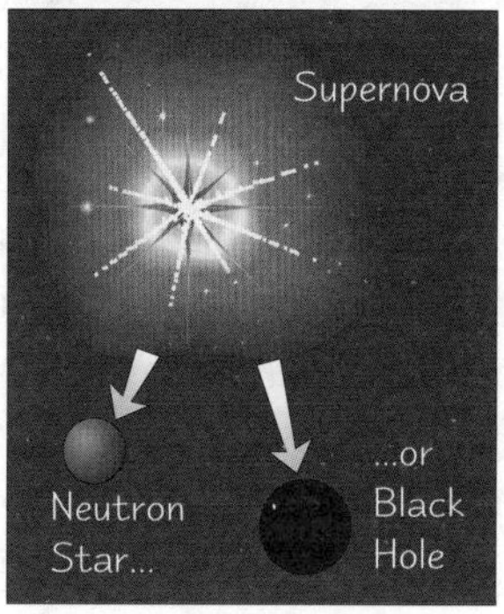

Massive Stars go out with a **Bit of a Bang**

1) When the core of a star runs out of fuel, it starts to **contract** — forming a white dwarf core.
2) If the star is **massive enough** though, it keeps contracting. This happens when the mass of the core is more than **1.4 times** the mass of the **Sun**.
3) The electrons get **squashed** onto the atomic **nuclei**, combining with protons to form **neutrons** and **neutrinos**.
4) The core suddenly collapses to become a **NEUTRON STAR**, which the outer layers fall onto.
5) When the outer layers **hit** the surface of the **neutron star** they **rebound**, setting up huge **shockwaves**, ripping the star apart and causing a **supernova**. The light from a supernova can briefly outshine an **entire galaxy**.

Neutron stars are incredibly **dense** (about 4×10^{17} kgm^{-3}).

They're **very small**, typically about 20 km across, and they can **rotate very fast** (up to 600 times a second).

They emit **radio waves** in two beams as they rotate. These beams sometimes sweep past the Earth and can be observed as **radio pulses** rather like the flashes of a lighthouse. These rotating neutron stars are called **PULSARS**.

Practice Questions

Q1 Describe how the Sun was formed.

Q2 Outline the main differences between the evolution of high mass and low mass stars.

Exam Question

Q1 This H-R diagram shows three of the main stages of stellar evolution. Use the H-R diagram to help you describe what occurs in the core of a low-mass star during its evolution. Describe the relative luminosity and temperature of the star at each stage.

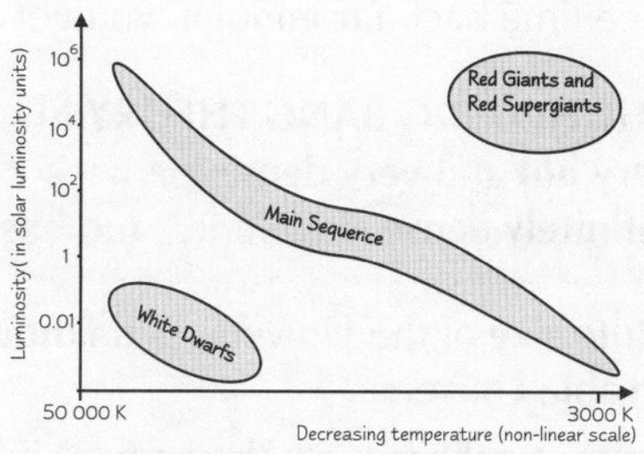

[7 marks]

Live fast — die young...

The more massive a star, the more spectacular its life cycle. The most massive stars burn up the hydrogen in their core so quickly that they only live for a fraction of the Sun's lifetime — but when they go, they do it in style.

Hubble and the Big Bang

Everyone's heard of the Big Bang theory — well here's some evidence for it.

The Doppler Effect — the Motion of a Wave's Source Affects its Wavelength

1) You'll have experienced the Doppler effect **loads of times** with **sound waves**.
2) Imagine an ambulance driving past you. As it moves **towards you** its siren sounds **higher-pitched**, but as it **moves away**, its **pitch** is **lower**. This change in **frequency** and **wavelength** is called the **Doppler shift**.
3) The frequency and the wavelength **change** because the waves **bunch together** in **front** of the source and **stretch out behind** it. The **amount** of stretching or bunching together depends on the **velocity** of the **source**.
4) When a **light source** moves **away** from us, the wavelengths of its light become **longer** and the frequencies become lower. This shifts the light towards the **red** end of the spectrum and is called **redshift**.
5) When a light source moves **towards** us, the **opposite** happens and the light undergoes **blueshift**.
6) The amount of redshift or blueshift is determined by the following formula:

$$z = \frac{\Delta\lambda}{\lambda} \approx \frac{\Delta f}{f} \approx \frac{v}{c} \quad \text{if } v << c$$

λ is the emitted wavelength, f is the emitted frequency, $\Delta\lambda$ and Δf are the differences between the observed and emitted wavelengths/frequencies, v is the velocity of the source in the observer's direction and c is the speed of light. ($v << c$ means "v is much less than c".)

7) The way cosmologists tend to look at this stuff, the galaxies aren't actually moving **through space** away from us. Instead, **space itself** is expanding and the light waves are being **stretched** along with it. This is called **cosmological redshift** to distinguish it from **redshift** produced by sources that **are** moving through space.
8) The same formula works for both types of redshift as long as v is much less than c. If v is close to the speed of light, you need to use a nasty, relativistic formula instead (you don't need to know that one).

Hubble Realised that the Universe is Expanding

1) The **spectra** from **galaxies** (apart from a few very close ones) all show **redshift**. The amount of **redshift** gives the **recessional velocity** — how fast the galaxy is moving away.
2) Hubble realised that the **speed** that **galaxies moved away** from us depended on **how far** they were away. A plot of **recessional velocity** against **distance** (found using Cepheid variables — see p. 53) showed that they were **proportional**, which suggests that the Universe is **expanding**.
3) This gives rise to **Hubble's law**:

$$v = H_0 d$$

where v = recessional velocity in **kms^{-1}**, d = distance in **Mpc** and H_0 = **Hubble's constant** in **kms^{-1}Mpc^{-1}**.

4) Since distance is very difficult to measure, astronomers disagree on the value of H_0. It's generally accepted that H_0 lies somewhere between 50 kms^{-1}Mpc^{-1} and 100 kms^{-1}Mpc^{-1}.
5) The **SI unit** for H_0 is s^{-1}. To get H_0 in SI units, you need v in ms^{-1} and d in m (1 Mpc = 3.09×10^{22} m).

The Expanding Universe gives rise to the Hot Big Bang Model

1) The Universe is **expanding** and **cooling down**. So further back in time it must have been **smaller** and **hotter**. If you trace time back **far enough**, you get a **Hot Big Bang**:

THE HOT BIG BANG THEORY: the Universe started off **very hot** and **very dense** (perhaps as an **infinitely hot**, **infinitely dense** singularity) and has been **expanding** ever since.

2) The **absolute size** of the Universe is **unknown** but there is a limit on the size of the **observable Universe**.
3) This is simply a **sphere** (with the Earth at its centre) with a **radius** equal to the **maximum distance** that **light** can travel during its **age**.

Leroy thought the Universe started with a big giant head that shot flaming arrows from its neck. All this big bang evidence is just circumstantial.

Hubble and the Big Bang

The **Age** and **Observable Size** of the **Universe** Depend on H_0

1) If the Universe has been **expanding** at the **same rate** for its whole life, the **age** of the Universe is $t = 1/H_0$ (time = distance/speed). This is only an estimate since the Universe probably hasn't always been expanding at the same rate.
2) Unfortunately, since no one knows the **exact value** of H_0 we can only **guess** the Universe's age.
If H_0 **= 75 kms⁻¹Mpc⁻¹**, then the age of the Universe $\approx 1/(2.4 \times 10^{-18}\ s^{-1}) = 4.1 \times 10^{17}$ s = **13 billion years**.

We **Can't Calculate** the **Age** of the Universe until we know its **Density**

1) All the **mass** in the Universe is attracted together by **gravity**.
This attraction tends to **slow down** the rate of expansion of the Universe.
2) The **critical density** is the density of mass in the Universe that means gravity is **just strong enough** to stop the expansion at $t = \infty$. With a bit of mathematical jiggery-pokery you can get an equation for the critical density of the Universe in terms of the **Hubble constant**:

$$\rho_0 = \frac{3H_0^2}{8\pi G}$$

3) If the density of the Universe is **less** than the critical density, gravity is **too weak** to stop the expansion. The Universe would just keep **expanding for ever**.
4) If the density is greater than the critical density, gravity would be **strong enough** to stop the expansion and start the Universe **contracting** again (ending up with a **Big Crunch**).
5) In fact if you look at the **graphs** of size against time, the **expansion rate** is **slowing down** in all three cases. So **all** three models suggest the Universe was expanding **faster in the past** than it is now.
6) If that's true, then we've **overestimated** the time it's taken for the Universe to get to the size it is now. The **more dense** the Universe is, the **younger** it must be.

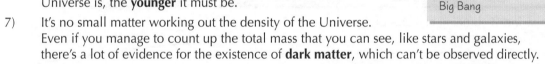

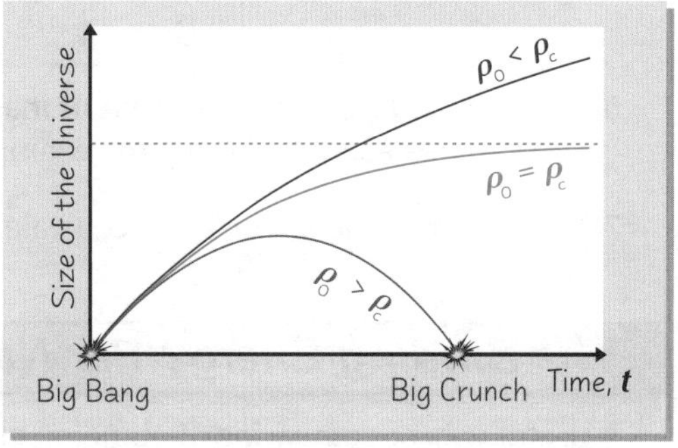

7) It's no small matter working out the density of the Universe.
Even if you manage to count up the total mass that you can see, like stars and galaxies, there's a lot of evidence for the existence of **dark matter**, which can't be observed directly.
8) If you include all the **dark matter** that's been detected **indirectly**, current **estimates** of the actual density aren't far off the **critical density**.
9) But even if we knew the **exact density** of the Universe, we could still be **none the wiser** about its future. Astronomers in the late 90s threw a spanner in the works — they found evidence that the expansion is now **accelerating**. That means the simple models on this page might be a long way from the true picture...

Practice Questions

Q1 Why does the calculated age of the Universe depend on its density?

Exam Questions

Q1 (a) State Hubble's law, explaining the meanings of all the symbols. [2 marks]

(b) What does Hubble's law suggest about the nature of the Universe? [2 marks]

(c) Assume H_0 = +50 kms⁻¹Mpc⁻¹ (1 Mpc = 3.09×10^{22} m).
Calculate an estimate of the age of the Universe, and hence the size of the observable Universe. [5 marks]

Q2 (a) An object has a redshift of 0.37. Estimate the speed at which it is moving away from us. [2 marks]

(b) Use Hubble's law to estimate the distance (in light years) that the object is from us.
(Take $H_0 = 2.4 \times 10^{-18}\ s^{-1}$, 1 ly = 9.5×10^{15} m.) [2 marks]

(c) With reference to the speed of the object, explain why your answers to a) and b) are estimates. [1 mark]

It's the end of the world as we know it...

Eeeshk... these pages are filled with questions that could leave anyone feeling critically dense. How did the Universe start? How old is it? Will it ever end? Just keep going through these pages and soon you'll feel like the Universe's personal psychic.

Nuclear Fission and Fusion

Stars get their energy from a nuclear reaction called fusion...

Nuclear Reactions Release **Binding Energy**

1) The **mass** of a **nucleus** is **less than** the mass of its **constituent parts** — the difference is called the **mass deficit**.
2) Einstein's equation, $E = mc^2$ (see p. 28), says that mass and energy are **equivalent**.
3) So, as nucleons join together, and the total mass **decreases**, the '**lost**' mass is **converted** to energy and **released**.
4) The amount of **energy released** is **equivalent** to the **mass deficit**.
5) If you **pulled** the nucleus completely **apart**, the **energy** you'd have to use to do it would be the **same** as the energy **released** when the nucleus formed. This is called the **binding energy** of the nucleus, and it's equivalent to the mass deficit.

Example Calculate the binding energy of the nucleus of a lithium atom, ^6_3Li, given that its mass deficit is 0.0343 u.

1) Convert the mass deficit into kg.
   Mass deficit = $0.0343 \times 1.66 \times 10^{-27} = 5.70 \times 10^{-29}$ kg
2) Use $E = mc^2$ to calculate the binding energy.
   $E = 5.70 \times 10^{-29} \times (3 \times 10^8)^2 = 5.13 \times 10^{-12}$ J = 32 MeV

Atomic mass is usually given in atomic mass units (u), where 1 u = 1.66×10^{-27} kg.

1 MeV = 1.6×10^{-13} J

6) The **binding energy per unit of mass deficit** can be calculated (using the example above): $\frac{\text{binding energy}}{\text{mass defect}} = \frac{32 \text{ MeV}}{0.0343 \text{ u}} \approx 931.3 \text{ MeV u}^{-1}$
7) So a mass deficit of **1 u** is equivalent to about **931.3 MeV** of binding energy.

The **Binding Energy Per Nucleon** is at a **Maximum** around **N = 50**

A useful way of **comparing** the binding energies of different nuclei is to look at the **binding energy per nucleon**.

$$\text{Binding energy per nucleon (in MeV)} = \frac{\text{Binding energy (B)}}{\text{Nucleon number (A)}}$$

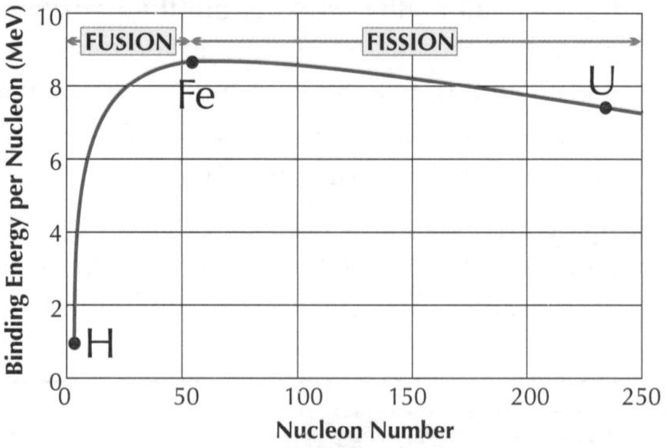

1) A **graph** of **binding energy per nucleon** against **nucleon number**, for all elements, shows a **curve**.
2) **High** binding energy per nucleon means that **more energy** is needed to **remove** nucleons from the nucleus.
3) The **most stable** nuclei occur around the **maximum point** on the graph — **nucleon number 56** (i.e. **iron**, Fe).
4) Looking at the graph, you can see that **combining small nuclei** (see p. 61) or **splitting large nuclei** (see below) **increases** the **binding energy per nucleon**, so **energy is released**.

Fission Means **Splitting Up** into **Smaller Parts**

1) **Large nuclei**, with at least 83 protons (e.g. uranium), are **unstable** and some can randomly **split** into two **smaller** nuclei — this is called **nuclear fission**.
2) This process is called **spontaneous** if it just happens **by itself**, or **induced** if we **encourage** it to happen.

Example

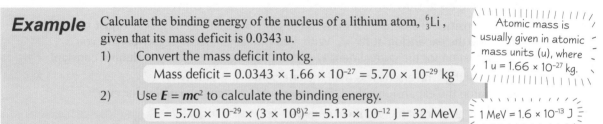

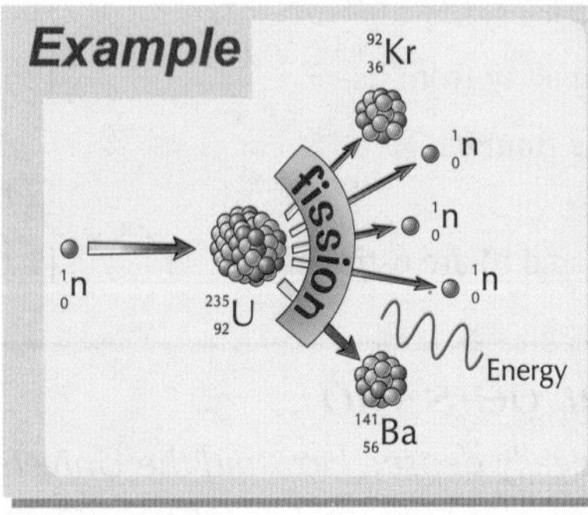

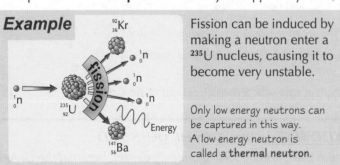

Fission can be induced by making a neutron enter a ^{235}U nucleus, causing it to become very unstable.

Only low energy neutrons can be captured in this way. A low energy neutron is called a **thermal neutron**.

3) **Energy is released** during nuclear fission because the new, smaller nuclei have a **higher binding energy per nucleon**.
4) In general, the **larger** the nucleus, the more **unstable** it will be — so large nuclei are **more likely** to **spontaneously fission**.
5) This means that spontaneous fission **limits** the **number of nucleons** that a nucleus can contain — in other words, it **limits** the number of **possible elements**.

Nuclear Fission and Fusion

Fusion Means Joining Nuclei Together

Two light nuclei can **combine** to create a larger nucleus and release a load of **energy**.
This is called **nuclear fusion**.

Example

In the Sun, **hydrogen nuclei** fuse in a series of reactions to form **helium**.

${}^2_1H + {}^1_1H \rightarrow {}^3_2He$ + energy

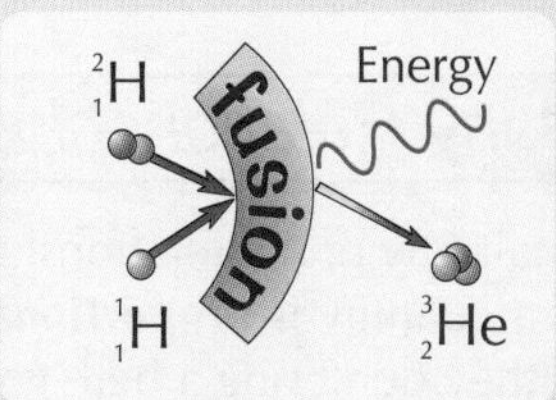

Nuclei Need Lots of Energy to Fuse

1) All nuclei are **positively charged** — so there will be an **electrostatic** (or Coulomb) **force** of **repulsion** between them.
2) Nuclei can only **fuse** if they **overcome** this electrostatic force and get **close** enough for the attractive force of the **strong interaction** to hold them together.
3) Typically they need about **1 MeV** of kinetic energy — and that's **a lot of energy**.

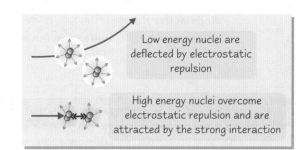

Low energy nuclei are deflected by electrostatic repulsion
High energy nuclei overcome electrostatic repulsion and are attracted by the strong interaction

Fusion Happens in the Core of Stars

1) The **energy** emitted by the **Sun** and other stars comes from nuclear **fusion** reactions.
2) Fusion can happen because the **temperature** in the **core of stars** is so **high** — the core of the Sun is about 10^7 K.
3) At these temperatures, **atoms don't exist** — the negatively charged electrons are **stripped away**, leaving **positively charged nuclei** and **free electrons**. The resulting mixture is called a **plasma**.
4) A lot of **energy** is released during nuclear fusion because the new, heavier nuclei have a **much higher binding energy per nucleon**. This helps to **maintain the temperature** for further fusion reactions to happen.

Practice Questions

Q1 What is the *binding energy per nucleon*?
Q2 Which element has the highest value of binding energy per nucleon?
Q3 What is spontaneous fission?
Q4 How can fission be induced in ^{235}U?
Q5 Describe the conditions in the core of a star. Why are these conditions necessary for fusion?

Exam Questions

Q1 The following equation represents a nuclear reaction that takes place in the Sun:

${}^1_1p + {}^1_1p \rightarrow {}^2_1H + {}^{0}_{+1}\beta$ + energy released   where p is a proton and β is a positron (opposite of an electron)

(a) State the type of nuclear reaction shown. [1 mark]
(b) Given that the binding energy per nucleon for a proton is 0 MeV and for a ^2H nucleus it is approximately 0.86 MeV, estimate the energy released by this reaction. [2 marks]

Q2 This equation shows the reaction between deuterium (^2H) and tritium (^3H): ${}^2_1H + {}^3_1H \rightarrow {}^4_2He + {}^1_0n$ + energy
Masses: Deuterium nucleus = 2.013553 u, tritium nucleus = 3.015501 u, helium nucleus = 4.001505 u and neutron = 1.008665 u.

(a) Calculate the total mass deficit for this reaction. [2 marks]
(b) How much energy is released in this reaction, if a mass deficit of 1 u releases 931 MeV of energy? [1 mark]

If anyone asks, I've gone fission... that joke never gets old...

Phew, until that last subsection I was wondering what all this smashing nuclei has to do with astrophysics and cosmology. Make sure you're down with the mass deficit and bezzers with the binding energy calculations — they're exam faves.

Exponentials and Natural Logs

Mwah ha ha ha... you've hacked your way through the rest of the book and think you've finally got to the end of A2 Physics, but no, there's this tasty titbit of exam fun to go. You can get asked to look at and work out values from log graphs all over the shop, from astrophysics to electric field strength. And it's easy when you know how...

Many Relationships in Physics are **Exponential**

A fair few of the relationships you need to know about in A2 Physics are **exponential** — where the **rate of change** of a quantity is **proportional** to the **amount** of the quantity left. Here are just a couple you should have met before (if they don't ring a bell, go have a quick read about them)...

Charge on a capacitor — the decay of charge on a capacitor is proportional to the amount of charge left on the capacitor: $Q = Q_o e^{(-t/RC)}$ (see p. 15)

Radioactive decay — the rate of decay is proportional to the **number of nuclei left** to decay in a sample: $N = N_o e^{(-\lambda t)}$ (see p. 43)

You can **Plot** Exponential Relations Using the **Natural Log, ln**

1) Say you've got two variables, ***x*** and ***y***, which are related to each other by the formula $y = ke^{-ax}$ (where ***k*** and ***a*** are constants).
2) The inverse of e is the natural logarithm, **ln**.
3) By definition, $\ln(e^x) = x$. So far so good... now you need some **log rules**:

$\ln(ab) = \ln a + \ln b$ $\ln\left(\frac{a}{b}\right) = \ln a - \ln b$ $\ln a^b = b \ln a$

When it came to logs, Geoff always took time to smell the flowers...

You need to learn these rules.

4) So, if you take the natural log of the exponential function you get:
$\ln y = \ln(ke^{-ax}) = \ln k + \ln(e^{-ax})$ ⟹ $\ln y = \ln k - ax$
5) Then all you need to do is plot ($\ln y$) against x, and Eric's your aunty:

You get a **straight-line** graph with (**ln *k***) as the ***y*-intercept**, and **–*a*** as the **gradient**.

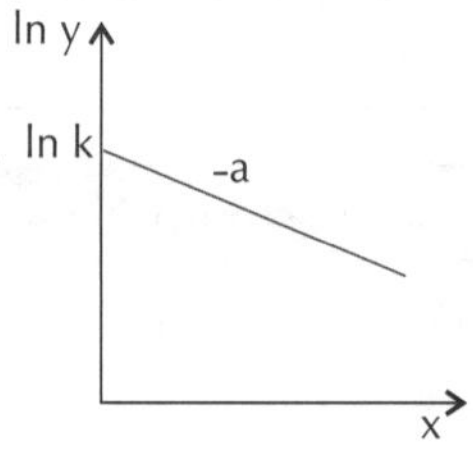

You Might be Asked to find the **Gradient** of a Log Graph...

This log business isn't too bad when you get your head around which bit of the log graph means what. On the plus side, they won't ask you to plot a graph like this (yipee) — they'll just want you to find the **gradient** or the **y-intercept**.

Example — finding the radioactive half-life of material X

The graph shows the radioactive decay of substance X.
(a) Find the initial number of atoms, N_o, in the sample.

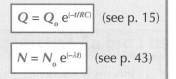

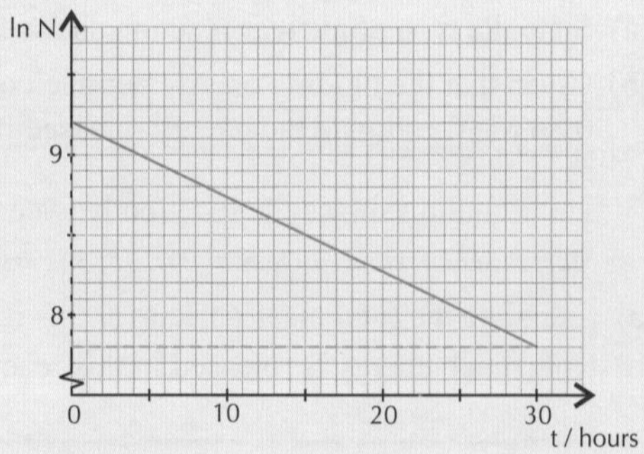

You know that the number of radioactive atoms in a sample, N, is related to the initial number of atoms by the equation $N = N_o e^{-\lambda t}$.

So, $(\ln N) = (\ln N_o) - \lambda t$ and $\ln N_o$ is the y-intercept of the graph = 9.2, $N_o = e^{9.2} \approx$ **9900 atoms**.

(b) Find the decay constant λ of substance X.

$-\lambda$ is the gradient of the graph, so: $\lambda = \frac{\Delta \ln N}{\Delta t} = \frac{9.2 - 7.8}{30 \times 60 \times 60} = \frac{1.4}{108\,000} = 1.3 \times 10^{-5}\ s^{-1}$(2s.f.)

Log Graphs and Long Answer Questions

You can Plot **Any Power Law** as a **Log-Log Graph**

You can use logs to plot a straight-line graph of **any power law** — it doesn't have to be an exponential.
Take the relationship between the energy stored in a spring, ***E***, and the spring's extension, ***x***:

$$E = kx^n$$

Take the log (base 10) of both sides to get:

$$\log E = \log k + n \log x$$

So **log *k*** will be the ***y***-intercept and ***n*** the gradient of the graph.

Example

The graph shows how the intensity of radiation from the Sun, ***I***, varies with its distance, ***d***.
I is related to ***d*** by the power law $I = kd^n$. Find ***n***.

$\log I = \log (kd^n) = \log k + \log d^n$
$= \log k + n \log d$.

so ***n*** is the **gradient** of the graph.
Reading from the graph:

$$n = \frac{\Delta \log I}{\Delta \log d} = \frac{15.4 - 5.4}{5 - 10} = \frac{10}{-5} = -2$$

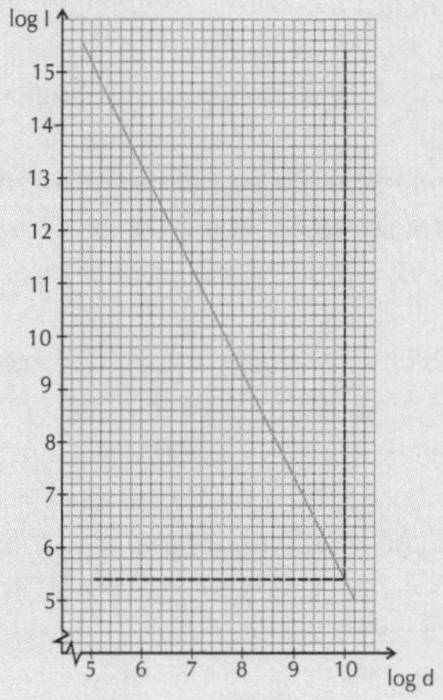

And that's the End of Logs... Now **Explain Yourself**...

In A2, they often give a couple of marks for 'the quality of written communication' when you're writing a slightly long answer (and not just pumping numbers into an equation). You can pick up a couple of easy marks just by making sure that you do the things in the fetching blue box.

1) **Explain** your ideas or argument **clearly** as this is usually what you'll get a mark for. And make sure you **answer the question** being asked — it's dead easy to go off on a tangent. Like my mate Phil always says... have I ever told you about Phil? Well he...
2) Write in **whole sentences**.
3) Use **correct spelling**, **grammar** and **punctuation**.
4) Also check how many marks the question is worth. If it's only a two-marker, they don't want you to spend half an hour writing an essay about it.

Example

A large group of people walk across a footbridge. When the frequency of the group's footsteps is 1 Hz, the bridge noticeably oscillates and 'wobbles'.
Fully describe the phenomenon causing the bridge to wobble.
Suggest what engineers could to do in order to solve this problem.
The quality of your written answer will be assessed in this question. *[6 marks]*

Good Answer

The pedestrians provide a driving force on the bridge causing it to oscillate. At around 1 Hz, the driving frequency from the pedestrians is roughly equal to the natural frequency of the bridge, causing it to resonate. The amplitude of the bridge's oscillations when resonating at 1 Hz will be greater than at any other driving frequency. The oscillations at this frequency are large enough to be noticed by pedestrians.

Engineers could fix this problem by critically damping the bridge to stop any oscillations as quickly as possible.

They could also adjust the natural frequency of the bridge so that it was not so close to a known walking frequency of large groups of people.

Bad Answer

resonance
driving frequency of group = nat. freq.
damping

There's nothing wrong with the physics in the bad answer, but you'd miss out on some nice easy marks just for not bothering link your thoughts together properly or put your answer into proper sentences.

Lumberjacks are great musicians — they have a natural logarithm...

Well, that's it folks. Crack open the chocolate bar of victory and know you've earnt it. Only the tiny detail of the actual exam to go... ahem. Make sure you know which bit means what on a log graph and you'll pick up some nice easy marks. Other than that, stay calm, be as clear as you can and good luck — I've got my fingers, toes and eyes crossed for you.

Answers

Unit 4: Section 1 — Further Mechanics

Page 5 — Momentum

1) *momentum before = momentum after [1 mark]*
(0.7 × 0.3) + 0 = 1.1$\mathbf{v}$
0.21 = 1.1$\mathbf{v}$ [1 mark for working] ⇒ $\mathbf{v}$ = 0.19 ms⁻¹ [1 mark]

2) *momentum before collision = momentum after collision*
(0.4 × 0.048) = (0.6 × 0.032) [1 mark]
0.0192 = 0.0192, so momentum is conserved [1 mark]

3) *Resolve the velocity vector into components parallel and perpendicular to the line of the collision:*
Parallel: $v_1 = 5 \times \cos(60°) = 2.5$ ms⁻¹ [1 mark]
Perpendicular: $v_2 = 5 \times \sin(60°) = 4.3$ ms⁻¹ [1 mark]
Find the momentum parallel to the line of the collision.
(0.6 × 2.5) + (2 × 0) = (0.6 × 0) + (2 × $\mathbf{v}$)
1.5 = 2$\mathbf{v}$ ⇒ $\mathbf{v}$ = 0.75 ms⁻¹ [1 mark]

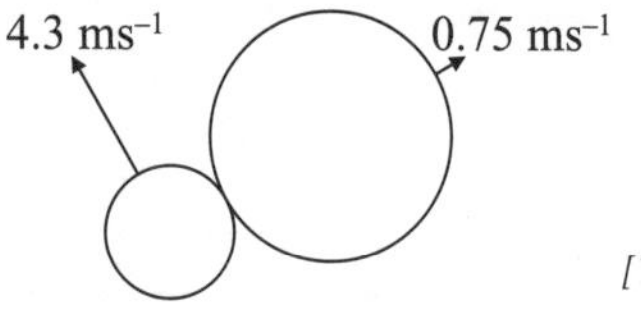

[1 mark for each vector]

Page 7 — Force and Energy

1) a) $\mathbf{KE} = \frac{1}{2}\mathbf{mv}^2$ and $\mathbf{PE} = \mathbf{mgh}$ [1 mark]. $\frac{1}{2}\mathbf{mv}^2 = \mathbf{mgh} \Rightarrow \frac{1}{2}\mathbf{v}^2 = \mathbf{gh}$
$\Rightarrow \mathbf{v}^2 = 2\mathbf{gh} = 2 \times 9.81 \times 2 = 39.24$ [1 mark]. $\mathbf{v}$ = 6.26 ms⁻¹ [1 mark]
b) 2 m — no friction means the kinetic energy will all change back into potential so he'll rise back to the same height as he started. [1 mark]
c) Put in some more energy by actively 'skating'. [1 mark]

2) a) The kinetic energy will be less after the collision. [1 mark]
b) total momentum before = total momentum after
10 000 × 1 = 25 000$\mathbf{v}$ [1 mark] so $\mathbf{v}$ = 0.4 ms⁻¹ [1 mark]
c) Before: KE = 0.5 × 10 000 × 1² = 5000 J [1 mark]
After: KE = 0.5 × 25 000 × 0.4² = 2000 J [1 mark]

Page 9 — Circular Motion

1) a) $\omega = \frac{\theta}{t}$ [1 mark] so $\omega = \frac{2\pi}{3.2 \times 10^7} = 2.0 \times 10^{-7}$ rad s⁻¹ [1 mark]
b) $\mathbf{v} = \mathbf{r}\omega$ [1 mark] = 1.5 × 10¹¹ × 2.0 × 10⁻⁷ = 30 kms⁻¹ [1 mark]
c) $\mathbf{F} = \mathbf{m}\omega^2\mathbf{r}$ [1 mark] = 6.0 × 10²⁴ × (2.0 × 10⁻⁷)² × 1.5 × 10¹¹
= 3.6 × 10²² N [1 mark]
The answers to b) and c) use the rounded value of ω calculated in part a) — if you didn't round, you answers will be slightly different.
d) The gravitational force between the Sun and the Earth [1 mark]

2) a) Gravity pulling down on the water at the top of the swing gives a centripetal acceleration of 9.81 ms⁻² [1 mark]. If the circular motion of the water needs a centripetal acceleration of less than 9.81 ms⁻², gravity will pull it in too tight a circle. The water will fall out of the bucket.
Since $\mathbf{a} = \omega^2\mathbf{r}$, $\omega^2 = \frac{\mathbf{a}}{\mathbf{r}} = \frac{9.81}{1}$, so ω = 3.1 rad s⁻¹ [1 mark]
$\omega = 2\pi\mathbf{f}$, so $\mathbf{f} = \frac{\omega}{2\pi} = 0.5$ rev s⁻¹ [1 mark]
b) Centripetal force = $\mathbf{m}\omega^2\mathbf{r}$ = 10 × 5² × 1 = 250 N [1 mark].
This force is provided by both the tension in the rope, $\mathbf{T}$, and gravity:
$\mathbf{T}$ + (10 × 9.81) = 250. So $\mathbf{T}$ = 250 – (10 × 9.81) = 152 N [1 mark].

Unit 4: Section 2 — Electric and Magnetic Fields

Page 11 — Electric Fields

1) a)

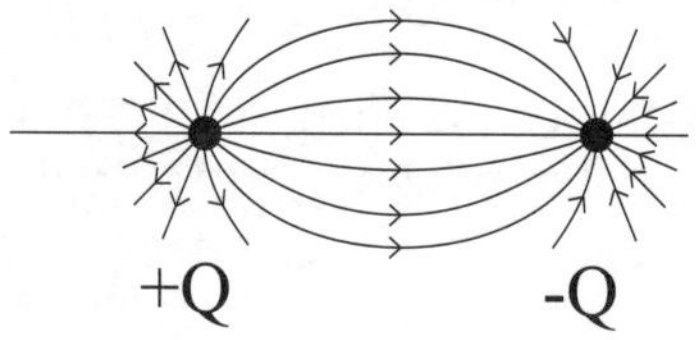

Recognisable pattern around the charges (not just in between) [1 mark], lines equally spaced around the charges and joined to the charges, and general symmetry of the diagram [1 mark], arrows along field lines between the charges with arrows pointing away from the positive and towards the negative charge [1 mark].

b) $\mathbf{E} = \frac{\mathbf{Q}}{4\pi\varepsilon_0\mathbf{r}^2}$ [1 mark]

$\mathbf{E} = \frac{2 \times 1.6 \times 10^{-19}}{4\pi \times 8.85 \times 10^{-12} \times (3.5 \times 10^{-10})^2}$ [1 mark]

$= 2.3 \times 10^{10}$ Vm⁻¹ or NC⁻¹ [1 mark]

2) a) $\mathbf{E} = \mathbf{V}/\mathbf{d}$ = 1500/(4.5 × 10⁻³) = 3.3 × 10⁵ [1 mark] Vm⁻¹ [1 mark]
The field is perpendicular to the plates. [1 mark]
b) $\mathbf{d}$ = 2 × (4.5 × 10⁻³) = 9.0 × 10⁻³ m [1 mark]
$\mathbf{E} = \mathbf{V}/\mathbf{d} \Rightarrow \mathbf{V} = \mathbf{Ed}$ = [1500/(4.5 × 10⁻³)] × 9 × 10⁻³ = 3000 V [1 mark]

Page 13 — Capacitors

1) a) Capacitance $= \frac{\mathbf{Q}}{\mathbf{V}}$ = gradient of line $= \frac{660\ \mu C}{3\ V} = 220\ \mu F$.
So the correct answer is **B** [1 mark]
b) Charge stored = $\mathbf{Q}$ = area = 15 × 10⁻⁶ × 66 = 990 μC.
So the correct answer is **D** [1 mark]

2) a) $\mathbf{W} = \frac{1}{2}\mathbf{CV}^2$ [1 mark] $= \frac{1}{2} \times 0.5 \times 12^2 = 36$ J [1 mark]
b) $\mathbf{Q} = \mathbf{CV}$ [1 mark] = 0.5 × 12 = 6 C [1 mark]

3) a) $\mathbf{W} = \frac{\mathbf{Q}^2}{2\mathbf{C}}$ [1 mark] $= \frac{(4.23 \times 10^{-3})^2}{2 \times 470 \times 10^{-6}} = 0.019035\ J \approx 0.02\ J$ [1 mark]
b) $\mathbf{V} = \frac{\mathbf{Q}}{\mathbf{C}}$ [1 mark] $= \frac{4.23 \times 10^{-3}}{470 \times 10^{-6}} = 9\ V$ [1 mark]

Page 15 — Charging and Discharging

1) a) The charge falls to 37% after $\mathbf{RC}$ seconds [1 mark],
so $\mathbf{t}$ = 1000 × 2.5 × 10⁻⁴ = 0.25 seconds [1 mark]
b) $\mathbf{Q} = \mathbf{Q}_0\mathbf{e}^{-\frac{t}{RC}}$ [1 mark], so after 0.7 seconds: $\mathbf{Q} = \mathbf{Q}_0\mathbf{e}^{-\frac{0.7}{0.25}} = \mathbf{Q}_0 \times 0.06$
[1 mark]. There is 6% of the initial charge left on the capacitor after 0.7 seconds [1 mark].
c) i) The total charge stored will double [1 mark].
ii) None [1 mark].
iii) None [1 mark].

Answers

Page 17 — Magnetic Fields and Force

1) a) $\mathbf{F} = \mathbf{BIl}$
$= 2 \times 10^{-5} \times 3 \times 0.04$ *[1 mark]*
$= 2.4 \times 10^{-6}$ N *[1 mark]*

b) $\mathbf{F} = \mathbf{BIl} \sin\theta$
$= 2.4 \times 10^{-6} \times \sin 30^{\circ}$
$= 2.4 \times 10^{-6} \times 0.5$ *[1 mark]*
$= 1.2 \times 10^{-6}$ N *[1 mark]*

Page 19 — Charged Particles in Magnetic Fields

1) a) $\mathbf{F} = \mathbf{Bqv} = 0.77 \times 1.6 \times 10^{-19} \times 5 \times 10^{6}$ *[1 mark]*
$= 6.16 \times 10^{-13}$ N *[1 mark]*

b) *The force acting on the electron is always at right angles to its velocity and the speed of the electron is constant. This is the condition for circular motion. [1 mark]*

2) a) $\phi = \mathbf{BA}$ *[1 mark]*
$= 2 \times 10^{-3} \times 0.23$
$= 4.6 \times 10^{-4}$ Wb *[1 mark]*

b) $\Phi = \mathbf{BAN}$ *[1 mark]*
$= 2 \times 10^{-3} \times 0.23 \times 150$
$= 0.069$ Wb *[1 mark]*

c) $$V = \frac{d\Phi}{dt} = \frac{(B_{start} - B_{end})AN}{t}$$
$$= \frac{(2\times10^{-3} - 1.5\times10^{-3})(0.23\times150)}{2.5} = 6.9\times10^{-3}\ \text{V}$$

[3 marks available for correct answer, otherwise one mark for each correct stage of working.]

Page 21 — Electromagnetic Induction

1) a) $\mathbf{V} = \mathbf{Blv}$ *[1 mark]*
$= 60 \times 10^{-6} \times 30 \times 100$
$= 0.18$ V *[1 mark]*

b) 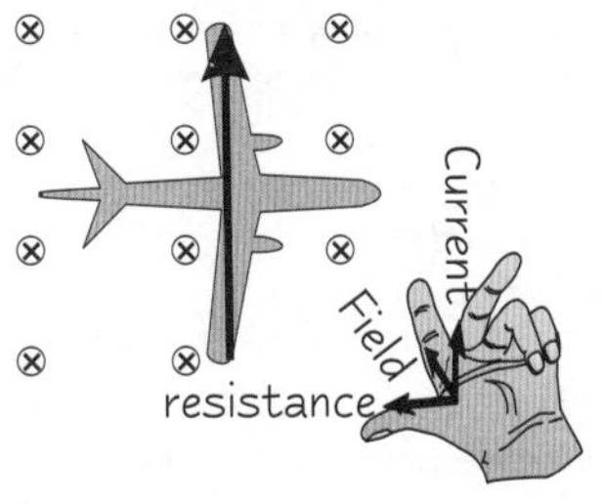

[1 mark]

2) *The graph should have three steps, with the last step twice the height of the others, with the opposite sign to the gradient of the flux change with time. So the correct answer is **B** [1 mark].*

Unit 4: Section 3 — Particle Physics

Page 23 — The Nuclear Atom

1) a) *The majority of alpha particles are not scattered because the nucleus is a very small part of the whole atom and so the probability of an alpha particle getting near it is small [1 mark]. Most alpha particles pass undeflected through the empty space around the nucleus [1 mark].*

b) *Alpha particles and atomic nuclei are both positively charged [1 mark]. If an alpha particle travels close to a nucleus, there will be a significant electrostatic force of repulsion between them [1 mark]. This force causes the alpha particle to be deflected from its original path [1 mark].*

Page 25 — Particle Accelerators

1) a) *1000 eV [1 mark]*

b) $1000\ \text{eV} \times 1.6 \times 10^{-19}\ \text{J/eV} = 1.6 \times 10^{-16}$ J *[1 mark]*

c) Kinetic energy $= \tfrac{1}{2}\mathbf{mv}^2 = 1.6 \times 10^{-16}$ J *[1 mark]*
$\mathbf{v}^2 = (2 \times 1.6 \times 10^{-16}) \div (9.1 \times 10^{-31})$
$= 3.5 \times 10^{14}$
$\Rightarrow \mathbf{v} = 1.9 \times 10^{7}\ \text{ms}^{-1}$ *[1 mark].*
Divide by 3.0×10^{8}: 6.3% of the speed of light *[1 mark]*

2) *The alternating electric field accelerates the particles from one side of the cyclotron to the other, increasing their energy [1 mark]. The magnetic field keeps the particles moving in a circular path [1 mark].*

3) $\lambda = \mathbf{h} \div \mathbf{p}$,
so $\mathbf{p} = \mathbf{h} \div \lambda = 6.63 \times 10^{-34} \div 0.15 \times 10^{-9}$
$= 4.42 \times 10^{-24}\ \text{kg ms}^{-1}$
$\mathbf{p} = \mathbf{mv}$,
so $\mathbf{v} = \mathbf{p} \div \mathbf{m} = 4.42 \times 10^{-24} \div 9.1 \times 10^{-31} = 4.86 \times 10^{6}\ \text{ms}^{-1}$
*So the correct answer is **B** [1 mark]*

Page 27 — Classification of Particles

1) *Proton, electron and electron antineutrino [1 mark].*
The electron and the electron antineutrino are leptons [1 mark].
Leptons are not affected by the strong interaction, so the decay can't be due to the strong interaction [1 mark].

2) *Mesons are hadrons but the muon is a lepton [1 mark].*
The muon is a fundamental particle but mesons are not [1 mark].
Mesons feel the strong interaction but the muon does not [1 mark].

Answers

Page 29 — Antiparticles

1) $e^+ + e^- \rightarrow \gamma + \gamma$ *[1 mark].*
This is called annihilation [1 mark].

2) *The protons, neutrons and electrons which make up the iron atoms would need to annihilate with their antiparticles [1 mark]. No antiparticles are available in the iron block [1 mark].*

3) *The baryon number is not conserved. / The creation of a particle of matter requires the creation of its antiparticle. In this case no antineutron has been produced [1 mark].*

4) *Energy before = energy after*
total energy for each particle before annihilation = $E_{rest} + E_{kinetic}$ *[1 mark]*
$E_{rest} = m_ec^2 = 9.11 \times 10^{-31} \times (3.0 \times 10^8)^2$
$= 8.2 \times 10^{-14}$ J $= 0.5$ MeV *[1 mark]*
$E_{tot} = 2 \times (300 \text{ MeV} + 0.5 \text{ MeV}) = 601$ MeV
Total energy of the two photons = 601 MeV
So the energy of 1 photon = 601 ÷ 2 = 300.5 MeV [1 mark]

Page 32 — Quarks

1) *The correct answer is **D**, uud [1 mark]*

2) $\pi^- = d\bar{u}$ *[1 mark]*
Charge of down quark = –1/3 unit.
Charge of anti-up quark = –2/3 unit.
Total charge = –1 unit [1 mark]

3) *The baryon number changes from 2 to 1, so baryon number is not conserved [1 mark]. The charge changes from +1 to +2, so charge is not conserved [1 mark].*

Page 35 — Detecting Particles

1) *Charged particles follow curved tracks in a magnetic field [1 mark]. +ve and –ve particle tracks curve in opposite directions [1 mark]. You can identify the direction of curvature for negative particles by looking for knock-on electrons OR by applying Fleming's left-hand rule. [1 mark]*

2) *Antineutrinos are neutral and so will not leave tracks in many standard detectors. Beta particles are charged and so will ionise particles and leave a track, and so are more easily detected. [1 mark]*

3) *The proton and the positive pion give tracks but the neutron and the neutral pion do not. So the correct answer is **C** [1 mark].*

4)

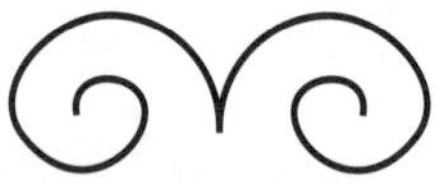

[1 mark for two tracks going in opposite directions, 1 mark for not showing a track for the photon, 1 mark for tracks spiralling inwards.]

5) $p = rBQ$ *[1 mark]*
$= 3.2 \times 1.8 \times 10^{-6} \times 1.6 \times 10^{-19}$
$= 9.2 \times 10^{-25}$ kgms^{-1} *[1 mark]*

Unit 5: Section 1 — Thermal Energy

Page 37 — Heat and Temperature

1) *Electrical energy supplied:*
$\Delta E = VI\Delta t$
$= 12 \times 7.5 \times 180$
$= 16200$ J *[1 mark]*
The temperature rise is 12.7 – 4.5 = 8.2 °C

Specific heat capacity: $c = \dfrac{\Delta E}{m\Delta\theta}$ *[1 mark]*

$= \dfrac{16200}{2 \times 8.2} = 988$ J kg^{-1} °C^{-1} *[1 mark]*

You need the right unit for the third mark — J kg^{-1} K^{-1} would be right too.

2) a) $pV = NkT$ *[1 mark], so* $N = \dfrac{pV}{kT} = \dfrac{1 \times 10^5 \times 10}{1.83 \times 10^{-23} \times 293} = 1.9 \times 10^{26}$

*[1 mark]. Now use the value of **N** to find **p** at the new height:*

$$p = \frac{NkT}{V} = \frac{1.9 \times 10^{26} \times 1.83 \times 10^{-23} \times 260}{25} = 35\ 500 \text{ Pa}$$ *[1 mark]*

We rounded the value of N in this calculation so it'd fit on the page — keep numbers like this in you calculator or you'll get huge rounding errors.

Page 39 — Internal Energy

1) a) *Mass of 1 molecule =* $\dfrac{\text{mass of 1 mole}}{N_A} = \dfrac{2.8 \times 10^{-2}}{6.02 \times 10^{23}}$
$= 4.65 \times 10^{-26}$ kg *[1 mark]*

b) $\dfrac{1}{2}m\overline{c^2} = \dfrac{3kT}{2}$ *Rearranging gives:* $\overline{c^2} = \dfrac{3kT}{m}$ *[1 mark]*

$\overline{c^2} = \dfrac{3 \times 1.38 \times 10^{-23} \times 300}{4.65 \times 10^{-26}} = 2.67 \times 10^5 \text{ m}^2\text{s}^{-2}$ *[1 mark]*

Typical speed = r.m.s. speed = $\sqrt{2.67 \times 10^5} = 517$ ms^{-1} *[1 mark]*

c) *Gas molecules move at different speeds because they have different amounts of energy [1 mark]. The molecules have different amounts of energy because they are constantly colliding and transferring energy between themselves [1 mark].*

2) a) *Speed =* $\dfrac{\text{distance}}{\text{time}}$ *so time =* $\dfrac{\text{distance}}{\text{speed}}$
The time = $\dfrac{8.0 \text{ m}}{400 \text{ ms}^{-1}} = 0.02$ s *[1 mark]*

b) *Although the particles are moving at an average of 400 ms^{-1}, they are frequently colliding with other particles. [1 mark] This means their motion in any one direction is limited and so they only slowly move from one end of the room to the other. [1 mark]*

c) *At 30 °C the average speed of the particles would be slightly faster [1 mark] since the absolute temperature would have risen from 293 K to 303 K and the temperature determines the average speed [1 mark]. This means the speed of diffusion would also be faster [1 mark].*

Answers

Unit 5: Section 2 — Nuclear Decay

Page 41 — Radioactive Emissions

1) Place different materials between the source and detector and measure the amount of radiation getting through [1 mark]:

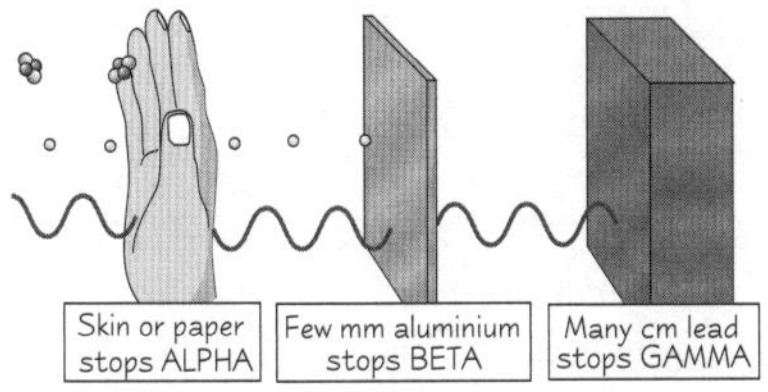

[1 mark for each material stopping correct radiation]

Page 43 — Exponential Law of Decay

1) The correct answer is ***C*** *[1 mark].*

2) a) Activity, A *= measured – background = 750 – 50 = 700 Bq [1 mark]*
$A = \lambda N \Rightarrow 700 = 50\,000\,\lambda$ *[1 mark] So* $\lambda = 0.014\ s^{-1}$ *[1 mark]*

b) $T_{\frac{1}{2}} = \frac{\ln 2}{\lambda} = \frac{0.693}{0.014} = 49.5$ seconds

[1 mark for the half-life equation, 1 mark for the correct half-life]

c) $N = N_0 e^{-\lambda t} = 50\,000 \times e^{-0.014 \times 300} = 750$

[2 marks available — 1 mark for the decay equation, 1 mark for the number of atoms remaining after 300 seconds]

Unit 5: Section 3 — Oscillations

Page 45 — Simple Harmonic Motion

1) a) Simple harmonic motion is an oscillation in which an object always accelerates towards a fixed point [1 mark] with an acceleration directly proportional to its displacement from that point [1 mark]. [The SHM equation would get you the marks if you defined all the variables.]

b) The acceleration of a falling bouncy ball is due to gravity. This acceleration is constant, so the motion is not SHM. [1 mark].

2) a) Maximum velocity = $(2\pi f)A = 2\pi \times 1.5 \times 0.05 = 0.47\ ms^{-1}$ *[1 mark].*

b) Stopclock started when object released, so $x = A\cos(2\pi f t)$ *[1 mark].*
$x = 0.05 \times \cos(2\pi \times 1.5 \times 0.1) = 0.05 \times \cos(0.94) = 0.029$ *m [1 mark].*

c) $x = A\cos(2\pi f t) \Rightarrow 0.01 = 0.05 \times \cos(2\pi \times 1.5t)$.
So $0.2 = \cos(3\pi t) \Rightarrow \cos^{-1}(0.2) = 3\pi t$. $3\pi t = 1.37 \Rightarrow t = 0.15$ *s.*
[1 mark for working, 1 mark for correct answer]

Don't forget to put your calculator in radian mode when you're solving questions on circular motion — it's an easy mistake to make.

Page 47 — Simple Harmonic Oscillators

1) a) Extension of spring = 0.20 – 0.10 = 0.10 m [1 mark]. Hooke's Law gives $k = \frac{\text{force}}{\text{extension}}$, *so* $k = \frac{0.10 \times 9.8}{0.10} = 9.8\ Nm^{-1}$ *[1 mark].*

b) $T = 2\pi\sqrt{\frac{m}{k}} \Rightarrow T = 2\pi \times \sqrt{\frac{0.10}{9.8}} = 2\pi \times \sqrt{0.01} = 0.63$ *s [1 mark].*

c) $m \propto T^2$ *so if* T *is doubled,* T^2 *is quadrupled and* m *is quadrupled [1 mark]. So mass needed = 4 × 0.10 = 0.40 kg [1 mark].*

2) E.g., $5T_{short\ pendulum} = 3T_{long\ pendulum}$, *and* $T = 2\pi\sqrt{\frac{l}{g}}$ *[1 mark]. Let length of long pendulum =* l*. So* $5\left(2\pi\sqrt{\frac{0.20}{g}}\right) = 3\left(2\pi\sqrt{\frac{l}{g}}\right)$ *[1 mark].*

Dividing by 2π *gives* $5 \times \sqrt{\frac{0.20}{g}} = 3 \times \sqrt{\frac{l}{g}}$. *Squaring and simplifying gives 5 = 9*l *so length of long pendulum = 5/9 = 0.56 m [1 mark].*

Page 49 — Free and Forced Vibrations

1) a) When a system is forced to vibrate at a frequency that's close to, or the same as its natural frequency [1 mark] and oscillates with a much larger than usual amplitude [1 mark].

b) See graph below. [1 mark] for showing a peak at the natural frequency, [1 mark] for a sharp peak.

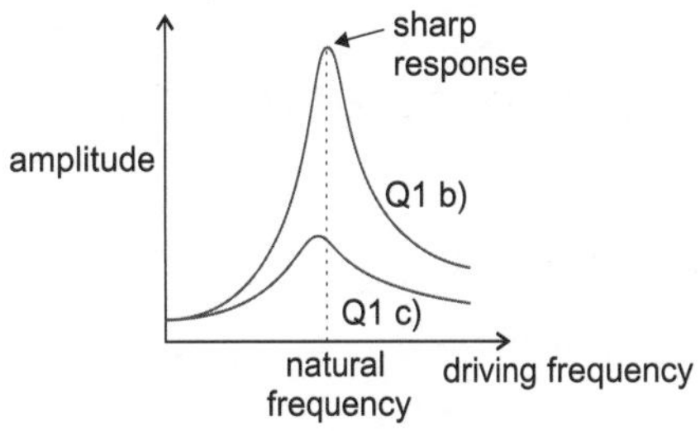

c) See graph. [1 mark] for a smaller peak at the natural frequency [the peak will actually be slightly to the left of the natural frequency due to the damping, but you'll get the mark if the peak is at the same frequency in the diagram].

2) a) A system is critically damped if it returns to rest in the shortest time possible [1 mark] when it's displaced from equilibrium and released.

b) e.g. suspension in a car [1 mark].

Answers

Unit 5: Section 4 — Astrophysics and Cosmology

Page 51 — Gravitational Fields

1) $g = \frac{GM}{r^2} \Rightarrow M = \frac{gr^2}{G} = \frac{9.81 \times (6400 \times 1000)^2}{6.67 \times 10^{-11}}$ *[1 mark]*
$= 6.02 \times 10^{24}$ kg *[1 mark]*

2) $g = \frac{GM}{r^2} = \frac{6.67 \times 10^{-11} \times 7.35 \times 10^{22}}{(1740 \times 1000)^2} = 1.62\ Nkg^{-1}$
*So the correct answer is **A** [1 mark]*

Page 53 — Measuring Astronomical Distances

1) a) *A standard candle is an object in space with a known luminosity. [1 mark] By knowing its luminosity and measuring the flux [1 mark], you can use the inverse square law to work out the distance to the object. [1 mark]*
b) *You could use the observed parallax of the star and the distance between the Earth and the Sun to make a right-angled triangle. [1 mark] The distance to the star could then be found using trigonometry. [1 mark]*

2) *The star is a sphere. So the luminosity of the star using Stefan's law is:* $L = A\sigma T^4$ *where A is the surface area of the star.*

$A = \frac{L}{\sigma T^4}$ *[1 mark]*

$= \frac{3.9 \times 10^{26}}{5.67 \times 10^{-8} \times 5500^4} = 7.5 \times 10^{18} m^2$ (to 2 s.f.) *[1 mark]*

Page 55 — Luminosity and the Hertzsprung-Russell Diagram

1) $T = \frac{2.898 \times 10^{-3}}{436 \times 10^{-9}} = 6650$ K to 3 s.f.
So the correct answer is **A** *[1 mark]*

2) a) *According to Wien's displacement law* $\lambda_{max} \times T = 2.898 \times 10^{-3}$*, so for this star* $\lambda_{max} = 2.898 \times 10^{-3} \div 4000 = 7.25 \times 10^{-7}$ *m [1 mark]. Curve **Y** peaks at around 0.7 μm (= 7×10^{-7} m), so could represent the star [1 mark].*
b) $L = \sigma AT^4$*, so* $3.9 \times 10^{26} = 5.67 \times 10^{-8} \times A \times 4000^4$ *[1 mark], which gives* $A = 2.7 \times 10^{19}\ m^2$ *[1 mark].*

3)

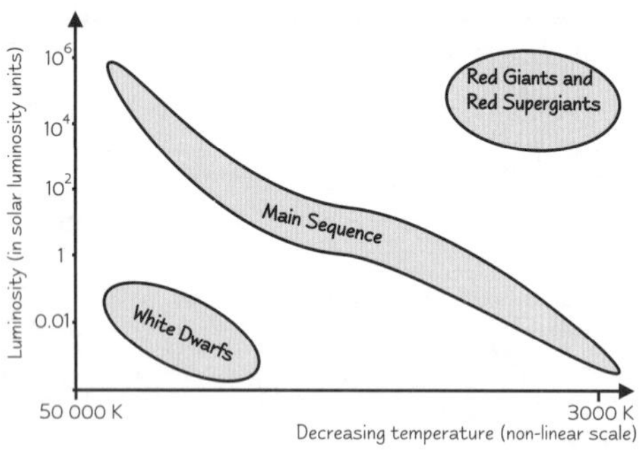

[5 marks maximum, 1 mark each for correctly labelled axes, 1 mark each for 'Main Sequence', 'White Dwarfs' and 'Red Giants'.]

Page 57 — The Life Cycle of Stars

1) *Stars on the main sequence are in a highly stable phase where they fuse hydrogen in their core [1 mark].*
Once the hydrogen in the core runs out, the star starts to collapse until the core becomes hot and dense enough to fuse helium [1 mark]. The rest of the star expands, and the star forms a red giant [1 mark]. Red giants have a higher luminosity and a lower surface temperature [1 mark] than main sequence stars.
Eventually the helium in the core will run out and the star will once again begin to collapse [1 mark]. The core will not become dense enough for further fusion to take place. The core will collapse to form a white dwarf and the star's outer layers will be ejected [1 mark]. White dwarfs have a lower luminosity and a higher surface temperature than main sequence stars [1 mark].

Page 59 — Hubble and the Big Bang

1) a) $v = H_0 d$ *[1 mark] where **v** is recessional velocity (in* kms^{-1}*), **d** is distance (in Mpc) and* H_0 *is Hubble's constant (in* $kms^{-1}Mpc^{-1}$*). [1 mark]*
b) *Hubble's law suggests that the Universe originated with the Big Bang [1 mark] and has been expanding ever since. [1 mark]*
c) $H_0 = v \div d = 50\ kms^{-1} \div 1$ *Mpc.*
$50\ kms^{-1} = 50 \times 10^3\ ms^{-1}$ *and 1 Mpc =* 3.09×10^{22} *m*
So, $H_0 = 50 \times 10^3\ ms^{-1} \div 3.09 \times 10^{22}\ m = 1.62 \times 10^{-18}\ s^{-1}$
[1 mark for the correct value, 1 mark for the correct unit]
$t = 1/H_0$ *[1 mark]*
$t = 1/1.62 \times 10^{-18} = 6.18 \times 10^{17}\ s \approx 20$ *billion years [1 mark]*
The observable Universe has a radius of 20 billion light-years. [1 mark]

2) a) $z \approx v/c$ *[1 mark] so* $v \approx 0.37 \times 3.0 \times 10^8 \approx 1.1 \times 10^8\ ms^{-1}$ *[1 mark]*
b) $d = v/H_0 \approx 1.1 \times 10^8 / 2.4 \times 10^{-18} = 4.6 \times 10^{25}$ *m [1 mark]*
$= 4.6 \times 10^{25} / 9.5 \times 10^{15}$ *ly = 4.9 billion ly [1 mark]*
c) $z = v/c$ *is only valid if* $v << c$ *— it isn't in this case [1 mark].*

Page 61 — Nuclear Fission and Fusion

1) a) *Fusion [1 mark]*
b) *The increase in binding energy per nucleon is about 0.86 MeV [1 mark]. There are 2 nucleons in* ^2H*, so the increase in binding energy is about 1.72 MeV — so about 1.7 MeV is released (ignoring the positron) [1 mark].*

2) a) *mass deficit = mass before – mass after [1 mark]*
= (2.013553 + 3.015501) – (4.001505 + 1.008665)
= 0.018884 u [1 mark]
b) *0.018884 × 931 = 17.6 MeV [1 mark]*

Index

Index